ELEMENTS

3	4	5	6	7	0
					4·003 **He** 2 Helium — 2

10·811 **B** 5 Boron 2)3	12·011 **C** 6 Carbon 2)4	14·007 **N** 7 Nitrogen 2)5	15·999 **O** 8 Oxygen 2)6	18·998 **F** 9 Fluorine 2)7	20·183 **Ne** 10 Neon 2)8
26·982 **Al** 13 Aluminium 2)8)3	28·086 **Si** 14 Silicon 2)8)4	30·974 **P** 15 Phosphorus 2)8)5	32·064 **S** 16 Sulphur 2)8)6	35·453 **Cl** 17 Chlorine 2)8)7	39·948 **Ar** 18 Argon 2)8)8

58·710 **Ni** 28 Nickel 2)8)16)2	63·540 **Cu** 29 Copper 2)8)18)1	65·370 **Zn** 30 Zinc 2)8)18)2	69·720 **Ga** 31 Gallium 2)8)18)3	72·590 **Ge** 32 Germanium 2)8)18)4	74·922 **As** 33 Arsenic 2)8)18)5	78·960 **Se** 34 Selenium 2)8)18)6	79·909 **Br** 35 Bromine 2)8)18)7	83·800 **Kr** 36 Krypton 2)8)18)8
106·400 **Pd** 46 Palladium 2)8)18)18	107·870 **Ag** 47 Silver 2)8)18)18)1	112·400 **Cd** 48 Cadmium 2)8)18)18)2	114·820 **In** 49 Indium 2)8)18)18)3	118·690 **Sn** 50 Tin 2)8)18)18)4	121·750 **Sb** 51 Antimony 2)8)18)18)5	127·600 **Te** 52 Tellurium 2)8)18)18)6	126·904 **I** 53 Iodine 2)8)18)18)7	131·300 **Xe** 54 Xenon 2)8)18)18)8
195·090 **Pt** 78 Platinum 2)8)18)32)17)1	196·967 **Au** 79 Gold 2)8)18)32)18)1	200·590 **Hg** 80 Mercury 2)8)18)32)18)2	204·370 **Tl** 81 Thallium 2)8)18)32)18)3	207·190 **Pb** 82 Lead 2)8)18)32)18)4	208·980 **Bi** 83 Bismuth 2)8)18)32)18)5	[210] **Po** 84 Polonium 2)8)18)32)18)6	[210] **At** 85 Astatine 2)8)18)32)18)7	[222] **Rn** 86 Radon 2)8)18)32)18)8

151·960 **Eu** 63 Europium 2)8)18)25)8)2	157·250 **Gd** 64 Gadolinium 2)8)18)25)9)2	158·924 **Tb** 65 Terbium 2)8)18)27)8)2	162·500 **Dy** 66 Dysprosium 2)8)18)28)8)2	164·930 **Ho** 67 Holmium 2)8)18)29)8)2	167·260 **Er** 68 Erbium 2)8)18)30)8)2	168·934 **Tm** 69 Thulium 2)8)18)31)8)2	173·040 **Yb** 70 Ytterbium 2)8)18)32)8)2	174·970 **Lu** 71 Lutetium 2)8)18)32)9)2
[243] **Am** 95 Americium 2)8)18)32)25)8)2	[247] **Cm** 96 Curium 2)8)18)32)25)9)2	[249] **Bk** 97 Berkelium 2)8)18)32)27)8)2	[251] **Cf** 98 Californium 2)8)18)32)28)8)2	[254] **Es** 99 Einsteinium 2)8)18)32)29)8)2	[253] **Fm** 100 Fermium 2)8)18)32)30)8)2	[256] **Md** 101 Mendelevium 2)8)18)32)31)8)2	254* **No** 102 Nobelium 2)8)18)32)32)8)2	[257] **Lw** 103 Lawrencium 2)8)18)32)32)9)2

GEORGE HERIOT'S
SCHOOL

Year	NAME	Class
19		
19		
19		
19		
19		
19		

CHEMISTRY TAKES SHAPE

BOOK THREE

CHEMISTRY

A. H. JOHNSTONE *and* T. I. MORRISON

B.Sc., A.R.I.C., Principal Chemistry Master
High School of Stirling

B.Sc., A.R.I.C., Lecturer in Chemistry
Jordanhill College of Education, Glasgow

HEINEMANN

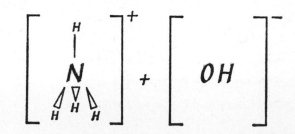

TAKES SHAPE

A complete course in chemistry for secondary schools in four volumes

BOOK THREE

EDUCATIONAL BOOKS LTD · LONDON

Heinemann Educational Books Ltd
London Melbourne Toronto Singapore Nairobi
Johannesburg Auckland Hong Kong Ibadan

S B N 435 64490 4 (limp bound edition)
S B N 435 64491 2 (loose leaf edition)

First published 1966
Reprinted with minor alterations 1967
Reprinted 1968

Published by Heinemann Educational Books Ltd, 48 Charles Street, London W.1
Printed in Great Britain by Morrison and Gibb Ltd, London and Edinburgh

LIST OF CONTENTS

v

1 PATTERNS IN ELECTRONS

1.1. What is a theory?

Chemistry cannot be understood without some idea of what molecules are, how they form and how they can be changed into other molecules. So we must begin this year by looking at the theory upon which a great deal of chemical thinking rests—the Atomic and Molecular Theory of Chemistry. In case you should mistrust the term 'theory' let us remind ourselves of how a chemical theory comes to be accepted.

(i) A number of experiments are done and observations are made.

(ii) A theory is put forward to explain these observations.

(iii) The theory is then tested by using it to predict the results of experiments which have not yet been performed. If the predictions are accurate, the theory is probably a good one. If the theory fails in some of its predictions, it has to be altered to include the new facts. By further testing and improving, a theory gains in importance and acceptance.

Last year we followed some of the reasoning which led up to our picture of an atom (Chemistry Takes Shape, Book II, Chapters 7 and 8). Let us beware of the word 'picture'. No one has ever seen an atom and so no one knows what atoms look like, but people find it convenient to visualise things and to think about them in 'pictures'. For example, we do not say that an atom *is* a sphere, but in many cases it is convenient to say that an

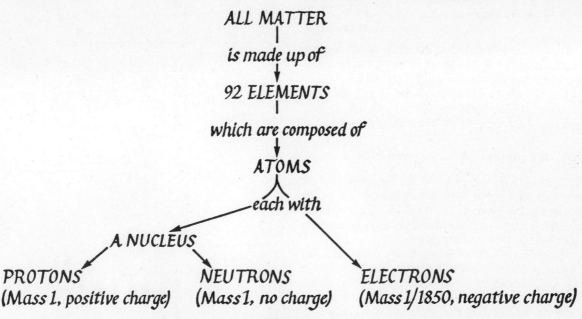

Figure 1

1

atom behaves *like* a sphere. All that we shall say about atoms in this book will be in terms of something with which you are already familiar.

The theory of the atom has been well tried and chemists are fairly sure that it is on the right lines.

1.2. What we already know about atoms

From our work last year, how much did we learn about atoms?

First of all we learned that atoms are composed of three main kinds of particles—protons, neutrons and electrons. Their properties are summed up in this chart (Figure 1).

Secondly, to keep an atom electrically neutral, the number of electrons is the same as the number of protons. This number is called the **Atomic Number**.

Thirdly, the mass of an atom is concentrated in its nucleus because that is where the protons and neutrons are located. The total number of protons and neutrons is called the **Mass Number**.

To Sum Up

In a neutral atom:

Mass Number = Number of protons + number of neutrons.

Atomic Number = Number of protons.
  = Number of electrons.

Mass Number − Atomic Number = Number of neutrons.

Lastly, we learned that the nucleus of an atom is concentrated in the heart of the atom and that the electrons move round the nucleus.

Let us now turn our attention to the electrons because it is their behaviour which largely dictates the properties of chemical substances.

1.3. A Problem of Accommodation

The electrons which surround the nucleus of an atom do not move around at random like wasps around a honey pot. They follow a very definite pattern in their arrangement. A simple analogy may help you to understand this.

Imagine a block of multi-storey flats, each flat having accommodation for two people only. On the first floor there is only one flat. On the second floor there are four flats and on the third nine flats. Assuming that the people who are going to occupy these flats will not share a flat if they can help it and that they are unwilling to climb any

more stairs than necessary, how will these flats be occupied?

The first tenant will occupy the flat on the first floor. The second tenant, to save climbing further, will share the flat with the first tenant (Figure 2).

The first floor is now completely filled and so the third tenant will have to go up to the second floor and occupy a room there.

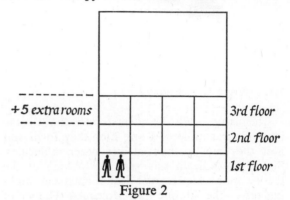

Figure 2

The next three people could each find a separate room on the second floor (Figure 3). Six people have now been accommodated. The next four will have to share rooms on the second floor until that floor is full.

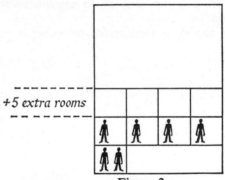

Figure 3

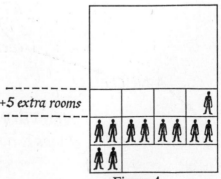

Figure 4

Ten people have now been fitted in, but an eleventh person will have to climb to the third floor to find accommodation (Figure 4) and so on.

Now this situation is not so far removed from the state of things in an atom. Electrons are arranged in 'shells' corresponding to the 'floors' in the building. Each shell has compartments where the electrons are to be found. Two, but not more than two electrons will share a compartment. If possible they occupy separate compartments provided it does not mean moving into a shell further from the nucleus.

Calculations have shown that these compartments seem to be sausage-shaped. The electrons are constantly on the move somewhere inside the sausage so that their negative charge is smeared out all over the sausage (Figure 5).

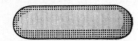

Figure 5

These sausage-shaped compartments are called electron pair clouds.

Now with these ideas in mind, let us see how electrons are accommodated in the simpler atoms at the beginning of the Periodic Table.

1.4. Electron Accommodation

Hydrogen ($^1_1$H) has only one electron and so it fits into the first shell. This is sometimes written 1).

Remember that the symbol $^1_1$H means that the atomic number (the number of protons) is one and the mass number is one. Similarly, $^4_2$He means that the atomic number is two and the mass number is four.

Helium ($^4_2$He) has two electrons which will have to share the only cloud in the first shell—written 2).

Lithium ($^7_3$Li) has three electrons two of which can be accommodated in the first shell, but the third will have to move out to the next shell—thus 2)1.

Beryllium ($^9_4$Be) will be 2)2.

Boron ($^{11}_5$B) will be 2)3.

Carbon ($^{12}_6$C) will be 2)4. In this atom all the clouds on the second shell are half-filled.

Nitrogen ($^{14}_7$N) will be 2)5. Three of the clouds in the second shell are half-filled and one is full.

Oxygen ($^{16}_8$O) will be 2)6.

Fluorine ($^{19}_9$F) will be 2)7.

Neon ($^{20}_{10}$Ne) will be 2)8 with all the clouds in the first and second shells filled.

In the third shell there are nine clouds but of these five are kept in reserve for later use. The other four are filled in the normal way.

$^{23}_{11}$Na	2)8)1.	$^{31}_{15}$P	2)8)5.
$^{24}_{12}$Mg	2)8)2.	$^{32}_{16}$S	2)8)6.
$^{27}_{13}$Al	2)8)3.	$^{35}_{17}$Cl	2)8)7.
$^{28}_{14}$Si	2)8)4.	$^{40}_{18}$Ar	2)8)8.

With the exception of the reserved clouds, the third shell is now full so that the electrons in $^{39}_{19}$K will be arranged 2)8)8)1 with the nineteenth electron forced out to the fourth shell. Calcium ($^{40}_{20}$Ca) will similarly be 2)8)8)2.

The five reserved clouds in the third shell now become available and the electrons in the ten elements from scandium to zinc fill up the unoccupied clouds in the third shell while the number in the fourth shell remains steady at two. Thus scandium has an electronic arrangement (or configuration) of 2)8)9)2 and zinc's arrangement is 2)8)18)2.

From gallium to krypton the fourth shell fills up to eight electrons giving, finally, $^{84}_{36}$Kr as 2)8)18)8.

You are probably asking how we know about the electron accommodation since no one has seen electrons in an atom. At this stage in your study of chemistry we cannot give you a full explanation, but here is some idea of how chemists find out about the electrons.

Last year during our study of sea water, we used flame tests. We found that several metal ions, when heated in a bunsen flame, gave a colour to the flame. It was pointed out that if the flame colours were observed through a spectroscope, a 'rainbow' of coloured lines appeared, each element having its own particular set of coloured lines. These spectra are a kind of chemical 'finger print'.

In your study of physics you may have learned that light is a form of energy and so these lines of coloured light in the spectroscope must correspond to changes in energy.

When a substance is heated its electrons take in heat energy and jump to an outer shell. They then tumble back to the inner shells giving out the energy they took in, but this time the energy is released as light. Different colours correspond to different amounts of energy. From these the physicist can calculate the difference in energy between the various shells and also find out how many electrons are in each shell.

This is not an easy task, for the physicist is involved in difficult and tedious calculations in his efforts to unravel the electronic arrangements.

Imagine that you were outside one of the blocks of flats described earlier. There is the sound of footsteps and bumps as the tenants run from floor to floor and then slide down the handrails. Suppose that from these sounds alone you were asked to find out how many tenants there were and which rooms they occupied. You now have some idea of the difficulty of the physicist's job in understanding the situation among the electrons. However, this work has been successfully accomplished and a very orderly pattern has emerged.

1.5. Atomic Volume

As you might expect, when electrons occupy a new shell, the volume of the atom will increase because the electrons in the new shell are further from the nucleus. Look at Figure 6 and compare the volumes of the lithium, sodium and potassium atoms. In each case a new shell has just been occupied and so the atomic volume increases.

However, look along the rows from left to right. Do you see that the volumes of atoms *decrease* from left to right—except the elements at the end of each row? Reading from left to right, each atom has one electron more than the atom to its left, that is, its atomic number is one more than that of the previous atom. But the atomic number is also the number of *protons* in the nucleus. Therefore, as we move from left to right the *nucleus* becomes more *positive*. This must have some effect on the electrons surrounding it since they are negatively charged. The nucleus must draw the electrons closer to itself as its positive charge increases and so the volume of the atom decreases. There is only a sharp increase when a shell is complete and a new one begins.

Summing up

1. Atomic volumes increase as we go down each column of the Periodic Table since each new row involves a new outer shell.

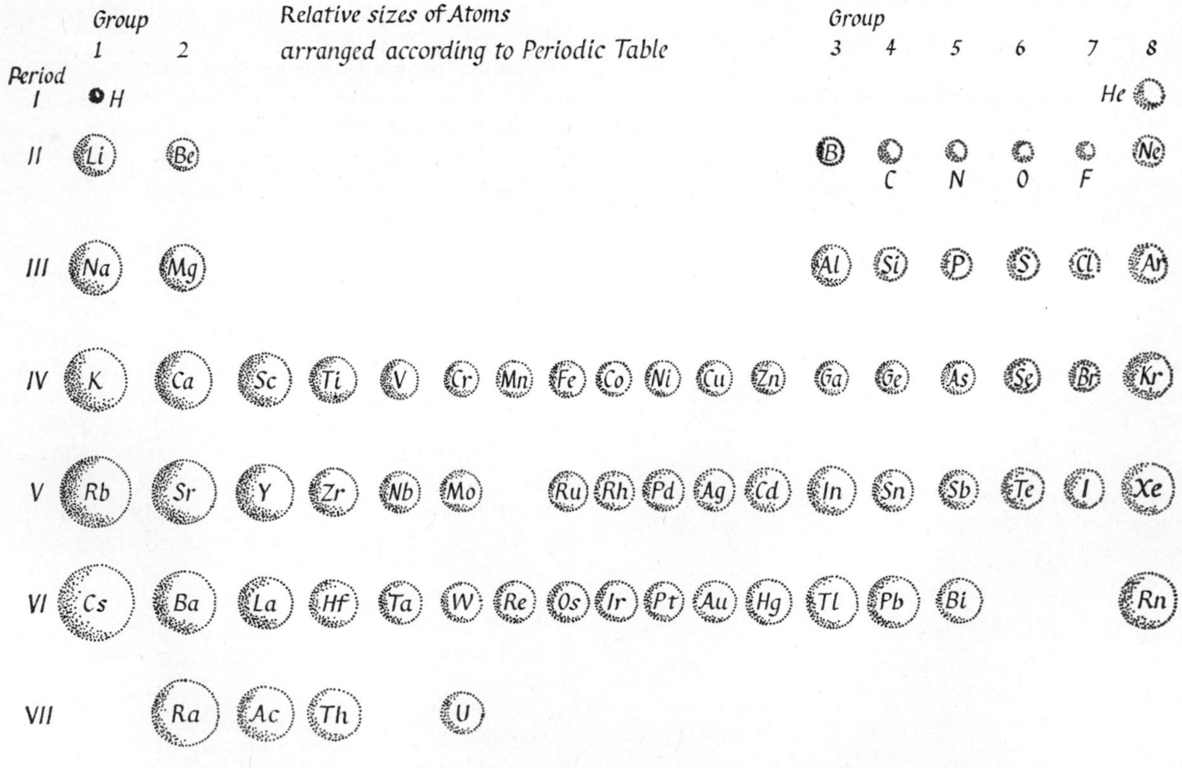

Figure 6

2. Atomic volumes decrease as we go from left to right along any one row of the Periodic Table because the increased charge on the nucleus is pulling the electrons closer to itself.

1.6. The Outer Shell

Look back at the electronic configurations on p. 3. What similarity do you see between the arrangements of electrons in lithium, sodium and potassium? Is there any similarity between chlorine, bromine and iodine? What about the noble gases helium, neon and argon?

You should not have to think back very far into your previous work to recall that lithium, sodium and potassium behave similarly in chemical reactions. Another group of elements which have chemical properties in common are chlorine, bromine and iodine.

It seems that the number of electrons in the outer shell of an atom has something to do with the chemical properties of that element.

When the outer shell contains eight electrons (or in the case of helium, two electrons) we have arrived at the noble gases.

The noble gases, you may remember, together make up about 1% of the air. Refer to the Periodic Table at the front of the book and remind yourself of the names of these gases. The noble gases used to be called the inert gases because it was thought that they did not combine with any other element, but in 1962 it was discovered that some of them did form compounds and so the name 'inert' could no longer apply. Nevertheless gases are almost completely inactive and it seems that a complete set of eight electrons on the outside shell makes these atoms very stable. This group of eight electrons is called the **stable octet.**

It seems then, that the chemical properties of elements are closely related to the number of electrons on the outside shell. Much of the work we do this year will be connected with the behaviour of these outer electrons.

LOOKING BACK AT CHAPTER 1

Before you leave this chapter, you should *know* and *understand* the meaning of the following:
1. Atomic Number.
2. Mass Number.
3. Electron Pair Cloud.
4. Atomic Volume.
5. Noble Gases and the Stable Octet.

Something to think about

If there are eight electrons on an outside shell, there must be four electron pair clouds. These clouds, being negatively charged, will repel each other. How will these four clouds arrange themselves in space?

HOW 2 ATOMS COMBINE

2.1.

In Chapter 1 it was mentioned that, in an atom, electrons are found in electron pair clouds. Each of these sausage-shapes can hold two, but not more than two electrons.

Let us consider what might happen when two atoms approach each other. Unless these are atoms of noble gases they will each have at least one half-filled cloud. Look back to 1.4, p. 3 and see why this statement is correct.

The most likely way for these atoms to combine will be through their half-filled clouds. Since these are clouds they can merge into each other.

Figure 7 shows only the half-filled clouds of the atoms of two elements A and B.

Figure 7

As they come together something like this could happen (Figure 8).

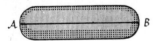

Figure 8

The overlapped clouds would merge to form one cloud between the atoms and in it would be found two electrons, one contributed by each atom.

Now let us turn our attention to the behaviour of the electrons inside this shared cloud. At least three things could happen.

(a) The atoms A and B could have an exactly equal share of the electrons as these electrons moved freely about in the cloud.

(b) The electrons could spend rather more of their time with atom B than with atom A. If you were to look for an electron, you would be more likely to find it nearer B than A.

(c) Both electrons could move on to atom B entirely and leave atom A without any share of them at all.

In the next chapter you will investigate these possibilities experimentally.

The links between atoms are called **bonds**. The three types of bond indicated above do exist and are called—

(a) **covalent bonds**—in which there is equal sharing of electrons.

(b) **polar covalent bonds**—in which there is unequal sharing of electrons.

(c) **electrovalent bonds**—in which one atom loses electrons to the other atom.

2.2. Electrons shared

Let us discuss these bonds a little further so that you will be able to decide how to detect them.

To obtain a perfectly *covalent bond* the atoms A and B would have to be identical. This means that they would have an equal pull on the pair of electrons. This is the kind of bond you would expect if two atoms of chlorine were to join.

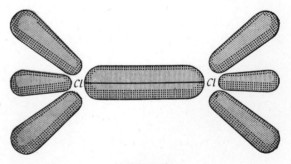

Figure 9

Chlorine has the electronic arrangement 2)8)7. On the outer shell there are three full and one half-filled clouds. If the half-filled clouds in each of the

6

atoms were to merge, the pair of electrons would be shared equally between them (Figure 9).

You can get some idea of this kind of bond if you take two large ring magnets of the same size. Add seven small ring magnets to each to represent the seven electrons on the outer shell of each atom. Slowly bring these 'atoms' closer to each other.

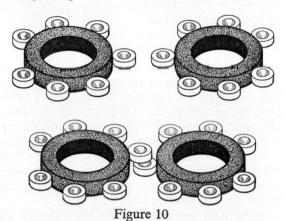

Figure 10

Eventually a pair of small rings will double up and become situated equally between the two large magnets (Figure 10).

This situation, with all the electron clouds filled, seems to make the chlorine molecule (the pair of chlorine atoms) more stable than the two separate chlorine atoms. Energy is released when a chlorine molecule is formed. To get the chlorine atoms apart requires a good deal of energy. Next year we shall do an experiment in which energy is used to split chlorine molecules back into chlorine atoms. *The covalent bond is a strong one.*

2.3. Unequal Sharing

The *polar covalent bond* is very like the purely covalent bond in its behaviour and it is fairly difficult to tell the two apart. We shall notice one of the effects of this kind of bond when we come to study the behaviour of water as a solvent in Chapter 14.5, p. 60.

Chemical compounds are formed by the combination of different kinds of atoms. It is likely that different atoms will have a different pull on electrons. There are millions of chemical compounds and so the polar covalent bond is bound to be very common.

In the bond, the electrons will tend to be found near the better electron attractor. Since electrons are negatively charged, one end of the bond will be a little more negative than the other. The sign

for slightly is δ (the small Greek letter delta). The bond between hydrogen and chlorine in hydrogen chloride gas is an example of this kind and the molecule is sometimes written as:—

$$\overset{\delta+}{H} - \overset{\delta-}{Cl}$$

δ+ means that the hydrogen, having less than its full share of the electrons, will have a slightly positive charge. The chlorine atom has a slightly larger share of the electrons and so it is shown as δ−.

The term covalent usually includes the polar covalent bonds.

2.4. Electrons lost and gained—*the electrovalent or ionic bond*

If a neutral atom loses one of its electrons it will have a positive charge because the number of protons will then exceed the number of electrons by one. Similarly, if an atom gains an extra electron, it will take on a negative charge.

We have already encountered charged atoms. What name is given to them? Do you recall the results of your electrolysis experiments earlier in the course? Search back into your laboratory notes. What kind of element appeared at the cathode? What charge must these ions have carried? What class of element appeared at the anode? What charge must these ions have carried?

Do you notice that the elements which form positive ions have few electrons on their outside shells while those that form negative ions have almost complete outer shells?

A model of the formation of the electrovalent or ionic bond can be constructed from two large ring magnets. To make them different, a 'buffer' of rubber tubing is fitted round one. Add one small ring magnet to the 'buffered' one and seven to the 'unbuffered' one (Figure 11 (a)). As these 'atoms' are brought closer together a small

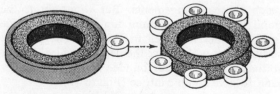

Figure 11 (a)

magnet will leave one large disc and jump on to the other (Figure 11 (b)).

Atoms cannot lose electrons easily because this involves pulling a negative particle (the electron)

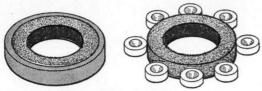

Figure 11 (b)

away from the attraction of the positive nucleus. To remove one electron from an atom requires a considerable amount of energy. For an atom to lose two electrons, a larger amount of energy is required and the loss of three electrons involves a great deal of energy. It is, therefore, not surprising that atoms with a large number of electrons on the outer shell do not lose all these electrons to other atoms. The effort would be far too great!

So why does the transfer take place at all?

If a sodium atom with the electronic arrangement 2)8)1 meets a chlorine atom, 2)8)7, we obtain a sodium ion 2)8 and a chloride ion 2)8)8. The sodium ion now has a positive charge (written Na^+) and the chloride ion a negative charge (written Cl^-).

Look back to 1.4, p. 3. What elements have the electronic arrangements 2)8 and 2)8)8? These elements are particularly stable. The ions may be

This attraction of positive for negative is the bond which holds the ions together. When the lattice forms (a settling process) a lot of energy is released which more than makes up for the energy expended in moving the electrons.

Figure 12

2.5. A comparison and a summary

When atoms are linked together by covalent bonds, there is little or no charge on the atoms. The bonds are strong inside the molecule. However, the molecules are self-contained and have very little attraction for neighbouring molecules.

In polar covalent compounds there are slight charges and so each molecule has a small attraction for its neighbours. This attraction is small compared with the strength of the covalent bonds inside the molecules.

When ions are formed they are attracted by *all* ions of the opposite charge. No one ion belongs to any other ion and so the bonds reach out all through the crystal lattice. There are no molecules because every ion 'belongs' to every other ion of the opposite charge.

Covalent	*Polar Covalent* $\delta+$ $\delta-$	*Electrovalent*
Cl : Cl Electrons equally shared. Strong bonds inside molecules, but little attraction between molecules.	H :Cl Electrons unequally shared. Strong bonds inside molecules. Some attraction between molecules.	Na^+ Cl^- Electrons transferred completely. Strong bonds to all ions of the opposite charge. No separate molecules.

more stable than the parent atoms when they reach these arrangements. But what about the bond between the sodium ion and the chloride ion? We met this idea in Form I. The positive sodium ions will attract the negative chloride ions so that each will be surrounded by six of the other kind to give a cubic lattice (Figure 12).

However, in a sodium chloride crystal the number of sodium ions is equal to the number of chloride ions and so we use the simple formula Na^+Cl^- to express this idea.

LOOKING BACK AT CHAPTER 2

Before you leave this chapter, you should *know* and *understand* the meaning of the following:
1. Overlapping of clouds.   2. Covalent bond.
3. Polar Covalent bond.   4. Electrovalent bond.

Something to think about

Silica is a covalent compound. From your work last year, what evidence is there that the covalent bonds in silica are strong?

THE EVIDENCE FOR IONS

If our theory about electrovalent compounds is correct, in our practical work we should expect to find evidence for the existence of ions. In the experiments which you are now going to carry out you should be looking for evidence of this kind.

3.1. Colour in common

What is the colour of copper (II) sulphate? Go to the chemical cupboard and find what colour most other sulphates are.

What is the colour of copper (II) nitrate? What is the colour of most other nitrates?

Collect as many other copper (II) salts as you can. What can you say about their colour? Can you suggest what the colour of the copper (II) ion might be? How very different copper ions must be from the copper atoms which make up a lump of metallic copper. In 1.2, p. 2 we pointed out that it was the electrons in an atom which dictated its chemical behaviour. Copper atoms, remember, give up two electrons and form positively charged copper (II) ions (2.4, p. 7). These ions have the nucleus of the original atom but a different number of electrons. It is the different number of electrons which gives rise to these quite different particles, copper ions.

You may also be able to find samples of sodium, potassium and ammonium dichromates. Are they all the same colour? What colour are most ammonium salts? What colour are most of the salts of sodium and potassium? Does this indicate anything about the colour of dichromate ions?

Your teacher may have samples of various compounds arranged on a board in order of the Periodic Table. You will see where the patches of colour lie and you should try to suggest what ions might be responsible for the colour.

3.2. When salts dissolve in water

Make a solution of copper (II) sulphate in one test-tube and of potassium ferrocyanide in a second. You already know the colour of the copper (II) ion. Remembering that most potassium salts are colourless, what is the colour of the ferrocyanide ion?

If you were to mix these two solutions what species of ions would there be in the mixture?

What happens when you do mix the two solutions? Can you suggest which ions are meeting to cause the formation of the solid? Look at potassium sulphate in the chemical cupboard.

Now half-fill a crystallising dish with water and set it on a piece of filter paper. Place a small crystal of copper (II) sulphate in the water at one side, and a small crystal of potassium ferrocyanide at the other. Is there any evidence for the diffusion of the ions?

After a few moments what do you see forming near the centre of the dish? Which ions have met there? Can you tell which of these two ions has moved through the water at a greater rate? Like diffusion in gases, this movement has taken place in all directions.

3.3. Some electrolyses

(a) Here is an experiment with copper dichromate in which you can see swarms of ions being forced to move in a particular direction.

Half-fill a W-tube with dilute nitric acid and carefully pour the copper dichromate solution, which your teacher has prepared for you, down the back limb. Try to make it form an even layer below the acid (Figure 13).

The beaker of cold water keeps the solution cool. Switch on the current and leave the arrangement for about 20 minutes. Bearing in mind your observations in 3.1 perhaps you can predict from the ionic theory what bands of colour might appear.

The current used must be 24v D.C. On no account should electricity from the mains be used directly.

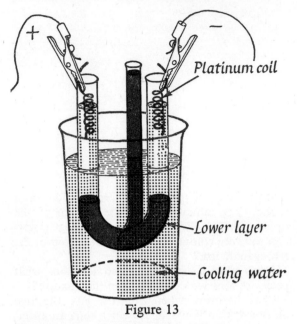

Figure 13

Does the result of this experiment bear out your observations on the colours of the copper (II) and dichromate ions?

(b) Do you remember what happened when you passed an electric current through a solution of copper chloride?

Any ions in the solution were not allowed to move freely this time. Their movement was affected by the presence of the electric field. Now, with the help of the ionic theory, we can suggest a possible explanation for what took place.

Copper (II) ions, the cations, moved in one direction when the current was switched on while the chloride ions, the anions, moved in the opposite direction. At the cathode, a **source** of electrons, copper (II) ions each gained two electrons and became atoms of copper. This type of change can be written:

$$Cu^{2+} \quad + \quad 2e \quad \rightarrow \quad Cu$$
a copper (II) ion   two electrons   a copper atom

The change involves a **gain** of electrons and is usually called **reduction** (or electronation). More will be said in Chapter 9.4 about this way of representing chemical changes.

The anode is positively charged. This means that it is short of electrons. We can think of it as an electron **sink** into which each chloride ion loses an electron and forms an atom of chlorine.

$$Cl^- \quad \rightarrow \quad Cl \quad + \quad e$$
a chloride ion   a chlorine atom   an electron

This change involves a **loss** of an electron and is usually called **oxidation** (or de-electronation).

Chemists know, however, that chlorine atoms

do not exist singly but go about in pairs, each pair of combined chlorine atoms forming a chlorine molecule (2.2, p. 6).

$$Cl \quad + \quad Cl \quad \rightarrow \quad Cl_2$$
Two single chlorine atoms   a chlorine molecule

The gas which you were able to smell at the anode during the electrolysis of copper chloride solution was composed of molecules of chlorine.

Behaviour of this kind during electrolysis is common to all solutions of electrovalent compounds in water. Remember the pattern. At the cathode, a **source** of electrons, positively charged ions or cations **gain** electrons. At the anode, an electron **sink**, negatively charged ions or anions **lose** electrons. The products at the cathode are either a metal or hydrogen, while only non-metals are given off at the anode.

3.4.   Turning ions loose

If sodium chloride contains ions, does the solid itself conduct an electric current? Can you devise an apparatus to help you answer the question? Try out the apparatus using a 6v battery as a source of electricity and a lump of rock salt.

Perhaps the ions in the solid are attracted to one another so rigidly that they are unable to move under the weak source of electrical energy which you are using. If this is so, how can we get the ions free to move? Do you remember earlier in the course we decided that dissolving was a breaking down process?

Perhaps spraying the lump of rock salt with a little water from a wash bottle may help. Try it.

Can you suggest any other way of getting the ions in the solid moving freely? What other breaking down process did we meet earlier? Perhaps the heat energy used to bring about melting might be capable of overcoming the strong attraction which the ions have for one another in the solid.

It so happens that sodium chloride has rather a high melting point, but Figure 14 shows an apparatus which you can use to test this idea using lithium chloride. It is very similar to sodium chloride but has a lower melting point.

Switch on the current and heat the lithium chloride in the crucible strongly until it melts. You will find a meker-type burner most suitable for this. The ammeter will tell you whether or not a current is flowing in the circuit.

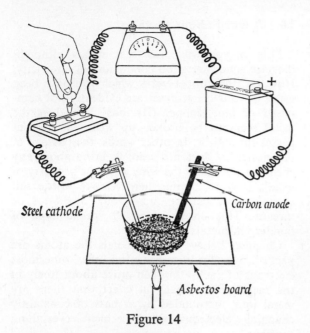

Figure 14

Does melting an electrovalent solid allow a current to flow?

What happens to the flow of current when you allow the molten solid to cool and solidify again?

Switch on the current and add a few drops of water to the cooled melt in the crucible. What happens?

Here is another surprise from water! How can a few drops of cold water succeed in doing what otherwise requires a large amount of heat energy? This is an important point to which we shall return in Chapter 14.

Now we have discovered two ways in which we can make an electrovalent compound conduct electricity. We can either melt the solid or dissolve it in water. In each case we are adding sufficient energy to the solid to break the lattice and allow the ions to move. Electrolysis can then take place, cations moving toward the cathode (−) and anions moving toward the electron sink, the anode (+).

Returning to the actual electrolysis of molten lithium chloride, what would you suggest might be the product at the anode? Repeat the experiment. Is there any evidence that this is so?

What might you expect to find on the cathode? Remember the position of lithium in the Periodic Table. What will happen to the metal if it comes into contact with the air? Switch off the current and place the tip of the cathode in a little water in a test-tube. Can you see any effervescence?

Thoroughly mix the contents of the tube and add two drops of phenolphthalein indicator. Is there any colour change? How do you explain your observations?

Your teacher may give you other salts which you can melt and then electrolyse in a similar way. You should attempt to identify any products at the electrodes with the help of the samples of elements which you have in the laboratory.

Not all of these compounds will dissolve in water so try only an electrolysis of the molten salt. In each case try to summarise the changes which take place at the electrodes, as was done in 3.3. Your teacher will give you the formulae for the ions present in the solids.

3.5. Electrovalent or Covalent?

According to our theory covalent compounds do not contain ions and so should not conduct electricity. Your teacher will provide you with some compounds which you can test to see if some are conductors and others non-conductors You can use the apparatus shown in Figure 15.

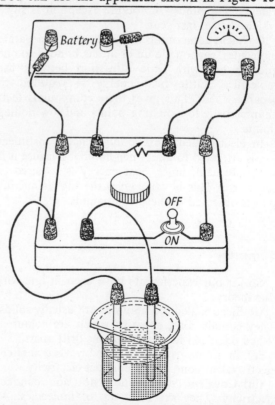

Figure 15

If the compounds are liquids test them directly, but if they are solids, dissolve them in water first.

As you test these substances arrange them in two groups—the conductors and the non-conductors.

Look at your conductors. How are they related to each other? You met them grouped together earlier in the course.

Did all of these substances conduct equally well? The good conductors are called strong electrolytes and the poorer ones are called weak electrolytes.

Let us turn our attention to the non-conductors (or non-electrolytes). Have they anything in common?

Covalent compounds, if they are not gases, are often liquids with a low boiling point. You may have noticed that as a result many covalent compounds are in narrow mouth reagent bottles! Most covalent compounds which are solid have a low melting point in comparison with electrovalent compounds. A notable exception is silica which we met last year.

Covalent compounds are composed of separate molecules, each made up of atoms bonded to one another but with little attraction between the molecules. Little heat energy is required to separate them. This gives these compounds their characteristic low melting points and low boiling points.

In electrovalent compounds, each constituent ion is attracted to all its neighbours. Because it is so firmly held, much heat energy is required to set it free. This is what gives the higher melting points observed in these compounds.

Summary

So far our experiments have been in line with our theory.

(i) Electrovalent compounds are usually solids. They contain ions, some of which are coloured. When dissolved in water the ions drift apart.

(ii) In solutions with water, or when molten, electrovalent compounds conduct electricity.

(iii) Covalent compounds do not conduct electricity. They are made up of molecules. At room temperature some are gases, others are liquids which are easily vaporised or solids which are readily melted.

3.6. A word about Metals

Most of you will know that metals, although they are solid, are good conductors of electricity. However, the copper wires which you have been using in your electrolyses are evidently not composed of blue copper (II) ions! Nor does the metal seem to be broken up when the current passes through it. In other words, the passage of the electricity does not seem to bring about any chemical change in the wire. Another property of metals is worth noting here. Unlike brittle salt crystals, they can be drawn out into wires or threads. This surely means a special type of bonding in metals.

Chemists believe that in metals the atoms are packed closely together and the outermost electrons of each atom can move about freely in the metal. This means in effect that there are metal ions surrounded by a mass of constantly changing electrons which cement everything together.

Because of the outer electrons moving throughout the mass, each ion is perfectly 'happy' wherever it is. There is no repulsion between the ions as there would be if these moving electrons were absent. Each layer of ions can be made to slip over the layer underneath (Figure 16) and so a

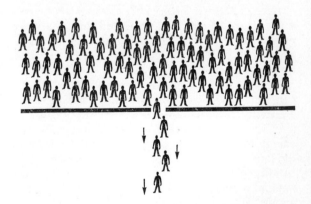

Figure 16

quantity of metal can be drawn out into a fine wire—in much the same way as a large crowd coming out of a football ground can be forced into a narrow file by being made to pass through a gate.

During the passage of electricity the metal remains electrically neutral because the free electrons move to the positive end while an equal number of electrons is being fed in from the negative end (Figure 17).

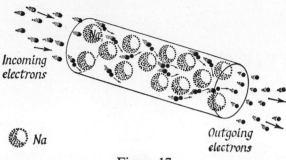

Incoming
electrons

Na

Outgoing
electrons

Figure 17

In this chapter the experiments which you have carried out support the predictions of the theories explained in Chapter 2. Therefore, as far as you have tested it, the ionic theory is satisfactory.

It is worth pointing out, however, that the ionic theory originally *followed* experiments such as the ones you have been carrying out. It developed during the late 19th century as chemists tried to explain the observed results of their experiments. We have put the theory before the experiments in this book because we believe that this way it is easier to understand.

You may have seen the appearance of what are known as chemical formulae on the bottles of chemicals which you have been using. It is now time to show you how a particular formula can be written.

LOOKING BACK AT CHAPTER 3

Before you leave this chapter, you should *know* and *understand* the meaning of the following:

1. Diffusion of Ions.
2. Cathode and Anode as Electron Source and Sink.
3. Reduction (or electronation).
4. Oxidation (or de-electronation).
5. Freeing Ions by melting and dissolving.
6. Electrovalent Compounds—their properties.
7. Covalent Compounds—their properties.
8. The Bonding in Metals.

Something to think about

Why should some electrovalent compounds be better conductors than others?

4 PATTERNS IN COMBINATION

4.1. Mixtures and Compounds

One of the main differences which we found between mixtures and compounds was the fact that the proportions of the components in a mixture could be varied while the components of a compound were in a fixed proportion.

How much salt is required to make a mixture of sand and salt? Only one crystal of salt need be added to a handful of sand to give a mixture of sand and salt. The other extreme would be to add a grain of sand to a handful of salt. Between these two extremes there are thousands of proportions possible and yet all are mixtures of sand and salt.

How much hydrogen and oxygen is required to make water? Every one gram of hydrogen requires eight grams of oxygen. This is fixed. Why is it that when elements combine, they do so in quite definite proportions? It must have something to do with the nature of the atoms themselves and so we must look back to Chapter 2 for our answer.

4.2.

Since we have mentioned water in the last section we could start with it.

It contains hydrogen and oxygen atoms only.

Oxygen atoms have *two* half-filled clouds in their outer shell and hydrogen has *one* half-filled cloud. By sharing electrons the hydrogen atom could help to fill one of the oxygen clouds. To fill the other one, another hydrogen atom would be required.

Thus we can see that oxygen requires the assistance of two—and only two—hydrogen atoms to help it fill its clouds.

∴ We write this as H_2O, 2 hydrogen atoms for every oxygen atom.

This chemical 'shorthand' for water (H_2O) is called a **formula**.

4.3. Clouds and Shape

Another interesting point arises out of this.

You may have noticed that the number of electrons on the outside shell of an atom normally does not exceed eight; that is, no more than four clouds in the outer shell. Since these four clouds each contain two electrons, they must be negatively charged. The four clouds must therefore repel each other.

We have mentioned that clouds are often sausage-shaped. A useful model would be sausage-shaped balloons. Blow up a long balloon, pinch it in the middle and turn the two portions in opposite directions to give a neck between them (Figure 18). These two lobes behave like two clouds in that they repel each other. If they are bent to touch each other, they spring apart when released.

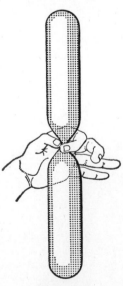

Figure 18

14

Do the same with another long balloon to give four lobes corresponding to the four clouds in the outer shell of an atom. Now twist the two balloons together so that they cross at the middle (Figure 19).

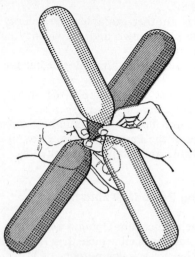

Figure 19

Like the four clouds, these four lobes will now repel each other to give an interesting geometrical shape (Figure 20).

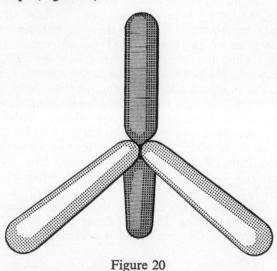

Figure 20

This is the arrangement into which, we believe, the clouds settle.

This shape must influence the shape of molecules. Let us return to our water molecule. Oxygen has six electrons on the outside shell and so two of its outer clouds are full and two are half-filled (Figure 21).

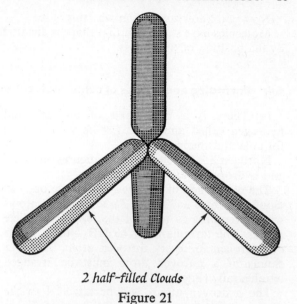

2 half-filled Clouds

Figure 21

When the two hydrogen atoms are attached, they will go on to the half-filled clouds giving the shape shown (Figure 22).

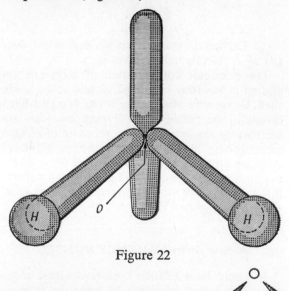

Figure 22

And so the water molecule will be  with the hydrogen atoms at an angle to each other.

Do you remember in first year seeing a model of a water molecule looking like this (Figure 23)?

Figure 23

Now you know the reason why this is so. Molecules have shape and that shape is dictated by the position of the clouds.

4.4. Formulae and shapes of other molecules

(a) There is a compound of nitrogen and hydrogen called ammonia. Let us work out its formula and shape.

Nitrogen has the electronic configuration of 2)5 and hydrogen is 1).

The outer shell of nitrogen must have one full cloud and three half-filled. *Three* hydrogen atoms will be required to help fill the *three* incomplete clouds. The formula must be NH_3—three atoms of hydrogen for every nitrogen atom. The four clouds of a nitrogen atom must be arranged tetrahedrally (Figure 24).

The hydrogen atoms will be attached to the three half-filled clouds giving the shape of Figure 25. The ammonia molecule is therefore something like a tripod,

(b) Carbon dioxide is a gas we studied last year. Let us apply this treatment to it.

The electronic configuration of carbon is 2)4 and so it has four half-filled clouds in the outer shell. Oxygen we already know has two half-filled clouds in the outside shell (Figure 26). Can you see that by sharing electrons, an atom of oxygen can only help fill two of the carbon atom's clouds? Another atom of oxygen is required to complete the filling of the clouds. The formula must therefore be CO_2—two atoms of oxygen for every atom of carbon (Figure 27).

4.5. A new term—*VALENCY NUMBER*

It would be a tedious business to have to go through all this reasoning to write the formula for a chemical substance and so we must find a simpler way of doing it.

Each element has a number (or sometimes more than one number) which tells us how many half-filled clouds there are in each of its atoms. Therefore we know how many electrons it is willing to share. In the case of metals the number tells us how many electrons one atom of it can be persuaded to lose from its outer shell. This number is called the **valency number** of the element.

Let us see this in action!

The valency number of silicon is *four* and the valency number of oxygen is *two* and therefore two atoms of oxygen will be required for each atom of silicon. The formula for silicon oxide must be SiO_2.

Here is another example. The valency number of magnesium is two and the valency number of chlorine one.

Therefore, magnesium chloride has the formula $MgCl_2$.

Notice that in a formula the small numbers refer to the element just in *front* of the number.

Where are these valency numbers to be found? They are in the Periodic Table. Look at the copy of the Table and study it carefully.

4.6. The Periodic Table helps

All the elements in Column I have one electron on the outside shell which they can lose and so they all have a valency number of 1.

Similarly, all the elements in Column II have two electrons on the outside shell which they can lose to fill the clouds on other atoms. They all have a valency number of 2.

The metals in the middle block from scandium to zinc have a valency number of 2 because you may remember (1.4, p. 3) that the number of electrons on the outside shell remains steady at two while the inner 'reserved' clouds are being filled up. However, in most cases these metals can move an electron from an inner shell to the outside shell (or vice versa). This means that these metals can have more than one valency number. For example, iron can have a valency number of 2 or 3. To distinguish the ions formed we write the iron (II) ion or iron (III) ion. Iron (II) chloride will have the formula $FeCl_2$ while iron (III) chloride will be $FeCl_3$.

Elements in Column III, that is the Column headed by boron, have a valency number of 3. Elements in Column IV have a valency number of 4.

In Columns V, VI and VII the number of half-filled clouds is given by subtracting the column number from 8. With the result that elements in Column V have a valency number of $8-5=3$. Elements in Column VI have a valency number of $8-6=2$, and elements in Column VII have a valency number of $8-7=1$.

Of course, the elements in Column VIII—the noble gases—have a valency number of $8-8=0$.

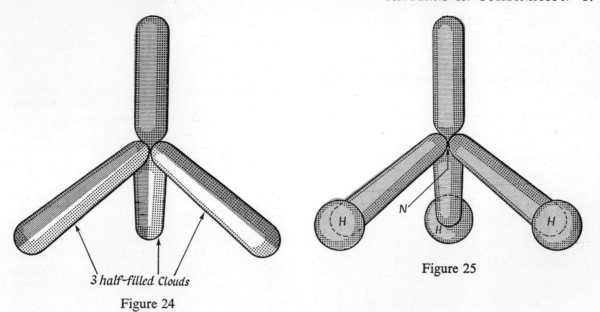

3 half-filled Clouds

Figure 24

Figure 25

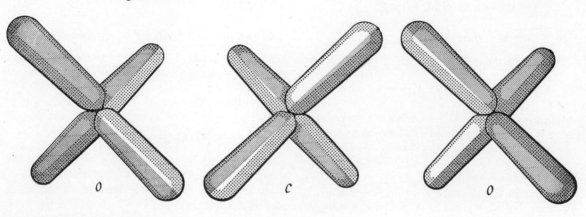

2 half-filled Clouds

4 half-filled Clouds

2 half-filled Clouds

Figure 26

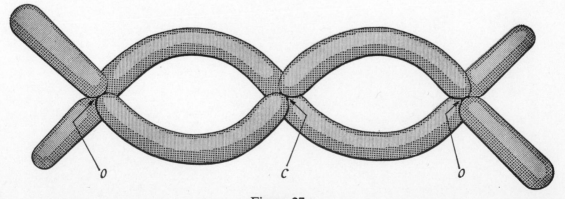

Figure 27

That means that they do not usually form any compounds.

Let us put this into practice.

(i) If you want to know the formula for *barium oxide* it is found like this.

> Barium—Column II ∴ valency number = 2
> Oxygen—Column VI ∴ valency number = 8 − 6 = 2.
> ∴ One atom of barium will 'satisfy' one atom of oxygen.
> ∴ Formula is BaO.

(ii) *Sodium sulphide*

> Sodium—Column I ∴ valency number = 1
> Sulphur—Column VI ∴ valency number = 8 − 6 = 2
> ∴ Two atoms of sodium are required for each atom of sulphur and so the formula for sodium sulphide is Na_2S.

(iii) *Aluminium Oxide*

> Aluminium—Column III ∴ valency number = 3
> Oxygen—Column VI ∴ valency number = 8 − 6 = 2.

Aluminium is able to lose *three* electrons but oxygen is able to accept only *two* electrons.

However, two aluminium atoms would lose *six* electrons which would be enough to fill the clouds of three oxygen atoms.

∴ Formula for aluminium oxide is Al_2O_3.

Perhaps by now you have noticed a simple trick for writing formulae. Let us look again at aluminium oxide.

Aluminium has a valency number of 3 and oxygen a valency number of 2. If these numbers are interchanged we have the formula Al_2O_3.

Similarly, the formula for calcium bromide would be obtained from calcium—valency number 2, and bromine—valency number 8 − 7 = 1. Interchange the numbers and we have the formula $CaBr_2$. As in algebra we do not write the number 1 in formulae.

Here is a list of compounds. See if you can write their formulae. If the element is one of those with more than one valency number, the valency number intended is shown in brackets after it.

Strontium chloride; sodium oxide; copper (II) sulphide; chromium (III) oxide; magnesium nitride; methane (hydrogen carbide); arsenic chloride; lead (II) iodide; caesium bromide; tin (IV) oxide.

LOOKING BACK AT CHAPTER 4

Before you leave this chapter, you should *know* and *understand* the meaning of the following:

1. Formula.
2. Valency Number.

Something to think about

1. Do electron clouds help you to understand the structure of diamond?
2. If electrical conductors have free electrons, how is graphite a conductor?

MORE ABOUT FORMULAE

5.1.

So far we have considered compounds containing two elements only: these are the compounds ending in **-ide**.

You already know that there are many compounds ending in **-ate** and even some ending in **-ite**. How are their formulae written? It would be very tedious indeed to work these out. To save a great deal of effort the following method is used.

Calcium carbonate is a compound containing three elements, one of which is oxygen. In this compound there is one metal ion and two non-metals. The non-metal ion—the carbon and oxygen together—has a valency number which covers both.

The carbonate ion containing one carbon and three oxygen atoms has a valency number of 2 because it is carrying two extra electrons. It is written CO_3^{2-}. The calcium ion comes from Column II of the Periodic Table and since it has been formed when a calcium atom lost two electrons, it must have a positive charge of 2. It is written Ca^{2+}.

The two positive charges on the calcium ion balance the two negative charges on the carbonate ion and so the formula is $Ca^{2+}CO_3^{2-}$.

Here is a list of common ions with their valency numbers shown as a number of charges. On electrolysis those with negative charges would move to the positive electrode, the **anode**, and so they are often called **anions**.

The ions from metals and the ammonium ion are positively charged. They are the **cations**.

Fluoride	F^-	Sulphate	SO_4^{2-}	Phosphate	PO_4^{3-}
Chloride	Cl^-	Sulphite	SO_3^{2-}		
Bromide	Br^-	Carbonate	CO_3^{2-}		
Iodide	I^-				
Nitrate	NO_3^-				
Nitrite	NO_2^-				
Hydroxide	OH^-				
Ammonium	NH_4^+				

Notice that the ions ending in **-ite** normally have one atom of oxygen less than the similar ion ending in **-ate**. Nit*rate*—NO_3^-, nit*rite*—NO_2^-. Sulph*ate*—SO_4^{2-}, sulph*ite*—SO_3^{2-}.

Let us try some examples.

Potassium nitrate

Potassium—Column I
—valency number 1
∴ ion is K^+.
Nitrate—NO_3^-. Since each has only a single charge, one potassium ion will balance one nitrate ion. ∴ $K^+NO_3^-$.

Magnesium sulphate

Magnesium—valency number 2 ∴ Mg^{2+}.
Sulphate—SO_4^{2-}.
The charges are equal ∴ Formula is $Mg^{2+}SO_4^{2-}$.

Copper (II) nitrate

Copper—valency number 2 ∴ Cu^{2+}.
Nitrate—NO_3^-.
Two nitrate ions will be required for each copper (II) ion ∴ Formula is $Cu^{2+}(NO_3^-)_2$.
The $_2$ outside the bracket means two nitrate ions. The bracket indicates that the *whole* nitrate ion (NO_3^-) has been multiplied by two.

Aluminium hydroxide

Aluminium—valency number 3 ∴ Al^{3+}.
Hydroxide—OH^-.
∴ Three hydroxide ions will be required for each aluminium ion giving $Al^{3+}(OH^-)_3$.

Chromium (III) Sulphate

Chromium—valency number 3 ∴ Cr^{3+}.
Sulphate—SO_4^{2-}.
Two chromium ions will have a total charge of 6+ and three sulphate ions will give a charge 6−.
∴ Formula is $(Cr^{3+})_2(SO_4^{2-})_3$.

You may have noticed that all of the compounds discussed in this section are **electrovalent**. They are all salts or bases. It is helpful to keep the charges on the ions in the formulae. Some books, however, miss these out, so do not be alarmed or surprised if you cannot find them. In **covalent** compounds there are no ions and so the formula contains only letters and numbers.

5.2. Formulae for acids

All acids are hydrogen compounds. Hydrogen has a valency number of one.

Hydrochloric acid (hydrogen chloride) is HCl
Nitric acid (hydrogen nitrate) is HNO_3
Nitrous acid (hydrogen nitrite) is HNO_2
Sulphuric acid (hydrogen sulphate) is H_2SO_4
Sulphurous acid (hydrogen sulphite) is H_2SO_3
Carbonic acid (hydrogen carbonate) is H_2CO_3
Phosphoric acid (hydrogen phosphate) is H_3PO_4

When a salt is formed, the acid gives the name of its anion part to the salt. Thus sulphuric acid (hydrogen sulphate) gives the name sulphate to all the salts formed from it. Similarly, nitric acid (hydrogen nitrate) gives the name nitrate to all the salts formed from it.

5.3. Why write formulae?

The material in this chapter has not been too easy and you may well have to spend some time going over it again. Your teacher will be able to give you many examples to work through until you have the ideas fixed in your mind. In a fairly short time you will find yourself writing formulae with ease. They are part of the language of chemistry and so it will pay you to understand and use them as soon as possible.

But you may be asking—why write formulae? Are they *just* a chemical shorthand? In many cases they are, but certainly not in every case.

It is much easier to write HCl instead of hydrochloric acid, but $K^+Al^{3+}(SO_4^{2-})_2.12H_2O$ is not shorthand for potash alum!

Imagine that someone places a bottle of white crystals in front of you with the label turned away from you. There is not much that you can tell about the crystals. The label is now exposed and you can see the name 'sodium carbonate'. You now have more information. You know that the crystals contain sodium ions and carbonate ions. Come closer and look at the small print and there you will find the formula which reads Na_2CO_3. $10H_2O$. (The formulae on labels do not usually show the charges on the ions.) You now have more information. Not only can you tell what elements are present, but you see that the crystals contain water. One other important piece of information is still there for you to find. For every two sodium ions there is one carbonate ion and ten molecules of water. We now have information about *quantities*.

5.4. Formulae and quantities

The information about quantities can be converted back from atoms to grams quite easily.

Let us take a simple example, the results of which you already know.

On the atomic weight scale ($^{12}_{6}C = 12$) the hydrogen atom weighs about 1 unit and the oxygen atom weighs 16 units. The exact atomic weights can be found in the Periodic Table at the front of the book.

$\therefore$ A water molecule (H_2O) weighs $(2 \times 1) + 16$ atomic weight units $= 18$ atomic weight units.

This is known as the **formula weight** of water.

$\therefore$ 2 a.m.u.* of hydrogen are combined with 16 a.m.u. of oxygen to give 18 a.m.u. of water.

Provided all the units are the same, we can use grams or pounds or even tons in place of units.

$\therefore$ 2 g of hydrogen are combined with 16 g of oxygen to give 18 g of water, or 1 g of hydrogen is combined with 8 g of oxygen to give 9 g of water. This was a result we found experimentally in the first year of the course. To be fair, we must point out that the formula of water was worked out from the weights in the first place and so it is not surprising that we should get the weights result by working backwards!

Let us now return to sodium carbonate and apply the same treatment.

The formula weight of sodium carbonate $Na_2CO_3.10H_2O$ must be 2×23 a.m.u. for sodium plus 12 a.m.u. for carbon and (3×16) a.m.u. for oxygen. The formula weight of water is 18 a.m.u. so in this case we must add (10×18) a.m.u. for water. This gives a total of 286 a.m.u.

What is the formula weight of carbon tetrachloride (CCl_4)? The answer is on the next page.

---

* Atomic weight units are sometimes called atomic mass units (a.m.u.). We shall use this abbreviation hereafter.

$$CCl_4$$
$$F.Wt = 12 + (4 \times 35 \cdot 5) \text{ a.m.u.}$$
$$= 154 \text{ a.m.u.}$$

There are some other examples of this type of calculation at the end of the chapter. Try them out for yourself.

5.5. What's in a *MOLE*?

On the atomic weight scale, a hydrogen atom weighs very nearly 1 unit.

How many hydrogen atoms are in 1 g of hydrogen? To find this we would have to divide one gram by the weight of one hydrogen atom. This has been done and it turns out to be an incredibly large number—more than a hundred thousand, million, million, million! This vast number is too difficult to handle and it has been given a name. Chemists call it a **mole**.

∴ 1 mole of a.m.u. = 1 gram

∴ 1 g of hydrogen contains a mole of hydrogen atoms.

Consider another element such as iron.
An atom of iron weighs 56 a.m.u.
How many atoms of iron are in 56 g of iron?
1 g = 1 mole of a.m.u. (see above)
∴ 56 g = 56 × 1 mole of a.m.u.
But each iron atom weighs 56 a.m.u.

∴ No. of atoms in 56 g of iron $= \dfrac{56 \times 1 \text{ mole}}{56}$

∴ 56 g of iron contains 1 mole of iron atoms.

In the case of aluminium, an atom weighs 27 a.m.u.

∴ 27 g of aluminium will contain a mole of aluminium atoms.

If we weigh out a number of grams of any element equal to the number of its atomic weight (that is, 56 g of iron or 27 g of aluminium or 12 g of carbon), the pile of the element obtained will contain a mole of atoms (Figure 28).

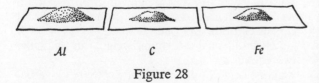

Al   *C*   *Fe*

Figure 28

The same idea applies to molecules of compounds. We calculated in 5.4 that the formula weight of carbon tetrachloride (CCl_4) was 154 a.m.u. ∴ 154 g of carbon tetrachloride must contain a mole of CCl_4 molecules; **or** 154 g of carbon tetrachloride must contain one mole of carbon atoms and four moles of chlorine atoms in combination.

Similarly, the formula weight of an electrovalent compound will contain definite numbers of ions. For example, sodium chloride (Na^+Cl^-) has a formula weight of 58·5 a.m.u. ∴ 58·5 g of sodium chloride will contain one mole of sodium ions and one mole of chloride ions.

The formula weight of sodium sulphate (($Na^+)_2SO_4^{2-}$) is 142 a.m.u. ∴ 142 g of sodium sulphate will contain two moles of sodium ions and one mole of sulphate ions.

LOOKING BACK AT CHAPTER 5

Before you leave this chapter, you should *know* and *understand* the meaning of the following:
1. Anions and Cations—their valency numbers.
2. **-ates** and **-ites**.
3. Formula Weight.
4. The Mole.

Try these examples:

1. Write the formula of barium chloride, iron (III) nitrate, calcium phosphate, ammonium carbonate.
2. What are the formula weights of magnesium sulphate, aluminium hydroxide, ammonium sulphate, sulphuric acid?
3. What is the weight of a mole of zinc atoms, carbon dioxide molecules, and acetic acid molecules ($C_2H_4O_2$)?
4. How many moles of atoms are there in 60 g of carbon, 16 g of copper, and 103·5 g of lead?
5. How many moles of molecules are there in 72 g of water, 5·5 g of carbon dioxide, and a spoonful of sugar ($C_{12}H_{22}O_{11}$) which weighs 5 g?

Something to think about

Someone has done this interesting calculation to give some idea of how large a mole is.

If all the land on the earth was a lawn with 10,000 blades of grass on each square foot, the earth would be covered with 2×10^{19} blades of grass. It would take 30,000 worlds like this to make room for a mole of grass blades!

This has been expressed in a humorous poem published in the *Journal of Chemical Education* of March, 1965, on page 126. Ask your teacher if he has a copy to show you.

FORMULAE AND EQUATIONS
6

6.1.

We began to use equations in the first year as a means of summing up chemical reactions. Our starting materials were written on the left of the equation and the products appeared on the right.

Copper (II) oxide+dilute hydrochloric acid→
copper (II) chloride+water.

It is a simple matter to substitute formulae for names in this equation and so obtain a *shorthand equation.*

$$Cu^{2+}O^{2-}+H^+Cl^-\rightarrow Cu^{2+}(Cl^-)_2+H_2O$$

The arrow means 'gives'.

You may be puzzled to see that we have written dilute hydrochloric acid as if it were an electrovalent compound. Look back at the results of 3.5, p. 11. Dilute acids conduct current and so they must contain free ions. In Chapter 5.2 we wrote acid formulae as if the acids were covalent. This apparent contradiction will be explained in 14.6, p. 61. Meantime, whenever we refer to dilute acids we shall show them as electrovalent compounds with free ions.

Here are some other examples.

(i) Zinc+dilute sulphuric acid→zinc sulphate
+hydrogen.

$$Zn+(H^+)_2SO_4^{2-}\rightarrow Zn^{2+}SO_4^{2-}+H_2$$

Notice that molecules of elements which are gases are shown with *two* atoms per molecule. H_2 for hydrogen, N_2 for nitrogen, O_2 for oxygen and so on. There are exceptions to this rule which we shall mention when the need arises. They are held together by covalent bonds in an effort to fill each other's half-filled clouds. See 2.2, p. 6 for the chlorine molecule.

(ii) Calcium carbonate+dilute nitric acid→
calcium nitrate+carbon dioxide+water.

$$Ca^{2+}CO_3^{2-}+H^+NO_3^-\rightarrow Ca^{2+}(NO_3^-)_2+CO_2+H_2O$$

But there is one very important thing about these equations which we have ignored. When we first met equations we had just met our first chemical law—The Law of Conservation of Matter. We noticed that the sum of the weights of the starting materials was equal to the sum of the weights of the products.

Let us look back at the first equation above.

$Cu^{2+}O^{2-}$	$+$	H^+Cl^-	$\rightarrow$	$Cu^{2+}(Cl^-)_2$	$+$	H_2O
$64+16$		$1+35\cdot5$		$64+71$		$16+2$
80		36·5		135		18
116·5				153		

The formula weights have been inserted and it can be seen that the sum of the weights of the reacting substances is not equal to the sum of the weights of the products.

The above equation is good as a shorthand way of summing up the reaction, but it is inadequate in providing us with information concerning weights.

Do you see that the weight of the left-hand side is 36·5 a.m.u. less than the weight of the right-hand side? The left-hand side is short of the formula weight of hydrochloric acid.

The equation would therefore give us more information if it were written thus:

$$Cu^{2+}O^{2-}+2H^+Cl^-\rightarrow Cu^{2+}(Cl^-)_2+H_2O$$

The large 2 in front of the HCl shows us that we need two formula weights of hydrochloric acid for each formula weight of copper oxide if we are going to make one formula weight of copper chloride and one of water.

Let us fill in the formula weights in the other two equations.

Zn	$+$	$(H^+)_2SO_4^{2-}$	$\rightarrow$	$Zn^{2+}SO_4^{2-}$	$+$	H_2
65	$+$	$2+32+(4\times16)$		$65+32+(4\times16)$	$+$	2
		98		161		
163				163		

The weights of the sides are equal and so this equation is said to be **balanced**.

$$Ca^{2+}CO_3^{2-} \;+\; H^+NO_3^- \;\rightarrow\; Ca^{2+}(NO_3)_2 \;+\; H_2O \;+\; CO_2$$

$$\underbrace{40+12+48}_{100} \quad \underbrace{1+14+48}_{63} \quad \underbrace{40+2(14+48)}_{164} \quad \underbrace{2+16}_{18} \quad \underbrace{12+32}_{44}$$

$$\underbrace{}_{163} \qquad \underbrace{}_{226}$$

This equation will balance only if we add 63 (or one formula weight of nitric acid) to the left.

$$Ca^{2+}CO_3^{2-}+2H^+NO_3^-\rightarrow Ca^{2+}(NO_3)_2+H_2O+CO_2$$

6.2

For many purposes a balanced equation is unnecessary. It is only required when we are concerned with the question of 'how much' material is involved in a chemical reaction. The balanced equation is important to manufacturers who want to calculate how much of a product can be made from a certain amount of raw material.

How much quicklime can be obtained from 5 tons of limestone?

$$Ca^{2+}CO_3^{2-} \;\rightarrow\; Ca^{2+}O^{2-} \;+\; CO_2$$

$$\underbrace{40+12+48}_{100} \qquad \underbrace{40+16}_{56} \qquad \underbrace{12+32}_{44}$$

$$\underbrace{}_{100}$$

This equation is balanced and is therefore of use in answering the question.

∴ 100 tons of limestone (calcium carbonate) will give 56 tons of quicklime (calcium oxide).

∴ 5 tons of limestone will give $\dfrac{56 \times 5}{100}$ tons of quicklime

$$= \textbf{\textit{2·8 tons}} \text{ of quicklime.}$$

How much copper can be expected from 2 g of copper oxide?

$$Cu^{2+}O^{2-}+H_2 = Cu+H_2O$$

$$\underbrace{64+16\; +2}_{80} \qquad \underbrace{64\; +2+16}_{18}$$

$$\underbrace{}_{82} \qquad \underbrace{}_{82}$$

This equation is balanced and so we can use it to calculate weights.

80 g $Cu^{2+}O^{2-}$ gives 64 g Cu

∴ 2 g $Cu^{2+}O^{2-}$ gives $\dfrac{64 \times 2}{80}$ g Cu

$$= \textbf{\textit{1·6 g}} \text{ Cu}$$

This is an equation which can easily be checked experimentally.

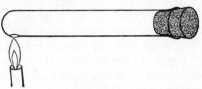

Figure 29

Firmly stopper a pyrex test-tube and heat it strongly near the closed end (Figure 29). As the glass softens the expanding air inside the tube will cause a blister to form where you are heating and eventually the blister will burst leaving the tube looking like the one in Figure 30.

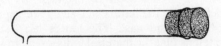

Figure 30

Fit the tube with a one-holed stopper carrying a length of glass tubing. Weigh the test-tube, stopper and tubing together. Insert about 1 g of dry, powdered copper oxide and reweigh all the apparatus. Using coal gas as a source of hydrogen, attach the tube to the gas tap and pass a *slow* stream of coal gas over the oxide. When the smell of gas is quite strong at the outlet of the tube, light it. If it is lit too soon, there may be a mild explosion. Why? Now gently warm the oxide for about ten minutes. (If a green colour is seen in the outlet flame a loss of copper ion is indicated [flame test] and the coal gas flow must be reduced.) Stop heating the tube, but allow the coal gas to continue passing through it until the tube is cold. Why is this done? Finally, reweigh the test-tube, copper, stopper and glass tubing.

Record your results like this.

(1) Weight of apparatus = g
(2) Weight of apparatus + copper oxide = g
(3) Weight of apparatus + copper = g
∴ Weight of copper oxide (2) − (1) = g
Weight of copper (3) − (1) = g
g of $Cu^{2+}O^{2-}$ gave g Cu
∴ 2 g of $Cu^{2+}O^{2-}$ gave g Cu
= g Cu

How does your result compare with the calculated result?

6.3. Equations with more information

Both the unbalanced and balanced equations discussed above have their uses. Each gives its own kind of information. By a simple addition to each equation, more information can be conveyed. Here is an example of what we mean.

Let us suppose that we want to give a short-hand description of a chemical reaction such as the following one:

'Some solid zinc was dropped into dilute hydrochloric acid. A solution of zinc chloride was left and hydrogen gas was given off.' The equation $Zn + H^+Cl^- \rightarrow Zn^{2+}(Cl^-)_2 + H_2$
or even $Zn + 2H^+Cl^- \rightarrow Zn^{2+}(Cl^-)_2 + H_2$
would give us no information about whether we were dealing with solids, liquids or gases. It would not tell us if the zinc chloride was in solution or in the form of crystals. To convey this idea we use the letters 's, l and g' to represent 'solid, liquid and gas'. The letters 'aq' (aqua = water) tell us that the material is dissolved in water.

$$Zn(s) + 2H^+Cl^-(aq) \rightarrow Zn^{2+}(Cl^-)_2(aq) + H_2(g)$$

This equation carries more information than those above.

An equation carrying even more information would be:

$$Zn(s) + 2H^+(aq) + 2Cl^-(aq) \rightarrow$$
$$Zn^{2+}(aq) + 2Cl^-(aq) + H_2(g)$$

It would tell us that the ions in the hydrochloric acid and in the zinc chloride were free in solution. This is what is meant by the extra plus signs between the ions.

We shall sum up now to clear the picture and to help you in your choice of equation for different situations.

Summing up

We have met three kinds of equation each with its own importance.

1. *Unbalanced equation* indicating the starting materials and the products of a reaction (Figure 31).
2. *Balanced equation* giving the above information but also telling us how much of each material is involved (Figure 32).
3. *State equation* which can be in the form of either 1 or 2 indicates the state in which each substance is.

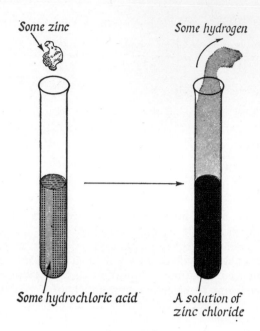

Figure 31

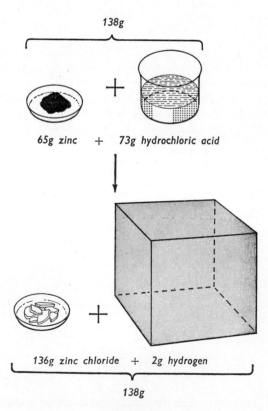

Figure 32

State equations can be very tedious and clumsy to write. In most cases the state of the substance is obvious. For instance, hydrogen will only be in the gas state in the laboratory and metals will seldom be molten. When the state is obvious we shall omit the state sign. If salts are in the solid, crystalline state we shall continue to add the letter (s). But if the salts are dissolved in water and the ions free in solution we shall omit the letters (aq). Molten salts will be followed by the letter (l).

For example, $Na^+Cl^-(s)$ will indicate solid sodium chloride while $Na^+ + Cl^-$ will mean a solution of salt in water with the ions free. Molten sodium chloride will be $Na^+(l) + Cl^-(l)$.

6.4. What an equation does not tell us

(i) It does not tell us if the reaction is fast or slow.

(ii) It often does not tell us if heat is required to make the reaction go.

(iii) It does not tell us how the reaction takes place.

For example, $2H_2 + O_2 \rightarrow 2H_2O(l)$ is the equation for the explosion of two volumes of hydrogen and one volume of oxygen to form water.

The equation does not show that it is an explosive reaction. It does not mention that unless the mixture is lit it will never react. Finally, it tells us nothing about the behaviour of the molecules. Do the oxygen molecules split and attach themselves to hydrogen molecules? Do the hydrogen and oxygen molecules collide and rearrange themselves as water molecules? The equation gives no answer to these questions.

In other words it tells us about the amounts and the physical states of the materials, but it says nothing about the route which the reaction takes.

Suppose that Tom and Mary went to a dance accompanied by John and Ruth. We saw them enter the hall and some hours later we saw them come out, but this time Tom and Ruth were together and John and Mary were together.

This could be represented by an equation such as—

$$TM + JR \rightarrow TR + JM$$

This would give the state of affairs before and after the dance, but it could tell us nothing about why the change of partners had taken place.

It does not tell us if there was a quarrel which resulted in the change nor does it tell us if it happened at the beginning of the evening or at the end. The equation conveys only the overall effect. We could read all sorts of unjustified happenings into the simple equation!

So it is with chemical equations. They are very useful, but they have their limitations. Because you can write an equation for a reaction do not imagine that you have thereby explained the reaction. If an equation is possible, it does not mean that the reaction is possible. An equation is an effort to represent *experimental facts*. We must never try to twist the facts to fit an equation.

And so although equations are useful in chemistry, they are limited in their use. *No more should be inferred from an equation than what it actually says.*

Later in this book you will meet other kinds of equation which will apply to special situations. These will be explained when we come to use them.

LOOKING BACK AT CHAPTER 6

Before you leave this chapter, you should *know* and *understand* the meaning of the following:
1. An Equation.
2. A Balanced Equation.
3. A State Equation.
4. What an Equation does **not** say.

Something to think about

1. How would it be possible to make $Cl_2(g)$ into $Cl_2(l)$?
2. Some reactions liberate heat. How would you show this in an equation?

EVIDENCE FOR A REACTIVITY SERIES

Now that you know something about chemical equations it would be a good idea to revise some of the reactions which you have met over the last two years. This will be useful revision and in addition will provide an opportunity for you to practice writing equations.

7.1. Metals and oxygen

Your teacher may quickly repeat the experiments you carried out in Form I in which you discovered the metals which combined most eagerly with oxygen. How many of these metals can you list, beginning with those which combine most fiercely with oxygen and ending with the so called noble metals, which apparently do not combine with oxygen?

Since this list of metals is in the order of their reactivity toward oxygen, we shall call it the **reactivity** series.

We saw that when hydrogen combined with oxygen to form water a great deal of energy was released as an explosion. To get the hydrogen back from the water all that energy had to be put back in again.

It would seem reasonable to suppose that if much energy is released when a certain metal combines with oxygen, the same amount of energy will have to be put back into the oxide to recover the metal. On the other hand, metals which liberate little energy in combining with oxygen will need little energy to recover them from the oxide.

We will try to obtain evidence for this idea later in the chapter.

7.2. Metals and water

Where, in the reactivity series, are the metals which react violently with cold water? Do you remember where they are found in the Periodic Table?

What did you have to do in order to get the less active metals to react with water? Perhaps you will be allowed to repeat these experiments to refresh your memory.

Which metals do not react with water? Where are they in the reactivity series?

7.3. Metals and hydrochloric acid

Can you remember adding small pieces of various metals to hydrochloric acid? Where, in the series, are the metals which reacted most violently with the acid? What gas was liberated during these reactions?

You might like to try this experiment to refresh your memory. To make a fair comparison between the metals weigh out one-hundredth of a mole of powdered magnesium, copper, tin, iron and zinc and put each into a separate test-tube. Each tube contains the same number of metal atoms. In a small beaker mix 15 ml concentrated hydrochloric acid with 15 ml of a detergent such as Teepol. Tip 6 ml of this mixture into each of the test-tubes containing the powdered metal. Are your results after five minutes anything like those shown in Figure 33?

The amount of foam produced is related to the rate of production of hydrogen which is, in turn, related to the reactivity of the metal.

In each case the metals have been giving electrons to any electron acceptors present and have become metal ions. The electron acceptors here are the hydrogen ions, H^+, in the acid solution. Each hydrogen ion can accept one electron and it

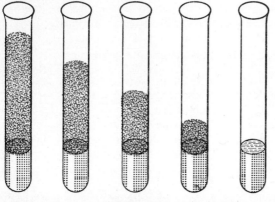

Figure 33

then becomes an atom of hydrogen. These atoms pair up to give molecules of ordinary hydrogen.

In the case of magnesium—

$$Mg \rightarrow Mg^{2+} + 2e$$
$$2e + 2H^+ \rightarrow H_2$$

Adding these gives—
$$Mg + 2H^+ \rightarrow Mg^{2+} + H_2$$

Since the chloride ions have nothing to do with the reaction we omit them from the equation.

Summarising

Potassium Sodium Lithium Calcium	Metals which displace hydrogen from cold water	Metals too reactive to risk in acid
Magnesium Aluminium Zinc Iron Tin Lead	Metals which displace hydrogen from steam	Metals which displace hydrogen from acid
Hydrogen Copper Mercury Silver Gold Platinum	Metals which do not displace hydrogen from water or from steam	Metals which do not displace hydrogen from acid

It should now be clear that if we know the position of a certain metal in the reactivity series, it should be possible to predict the rate of certain reactions in which the metal takes part.

7.4. Predictions from the series

On various occasions you have tried to obtain metals from metal oxides using both coal gas and charcoal. Where in the reactivity series are the metals which you obtained? Was there much energy involved in the combination of these metals with oxygen (7.1, p. 26)?

Evidently the metals which are most easily obtained from their oxides are at the bottom of the reactivity series. As you read the list from the bottom upwards, it becomes more and more difficult to obtain the metal. In the laboratory the metals above iron cannot be recovered from their oxides using either coal gas or charcoal. Do you remember how these metals can be obtained from their compounds?

Have you ever thought how some aspects of our civilisation have been dictated by chemistry? The discovery of metals is an interesting example of this.

During the Stone Age no metals had been discovered. Can you imagine life without metals? One of the first to receive man's attention was gold, a metal found uncombined in the earth. Many beautiful ornaments dating from the earliest civilisations several thousand years ago remain today in perfect condition.

Next to appear were the metals which could be obtained from their compounds relatively easily. Possibly at the beginning of the Bronze Age, about 5,000 years ago, someone heated a green mineral in an open fire and stirred it along with the hot ashes. When the fire died, he found a brown substance which could be beaten into shape. Impure copper had been discovered!

Bronze Age man became skilled in smelting his new found metal and in shaping it in moulds.

As his skill increased he learned to extract iron which required higher temperatures to smelt it. Thus the Iron Age began. Man was now able to make better tools and weapons with which to make new conquests.

As man's knowledge and ability to work metals have increased over the years, so has the number of metals which he has been able to isolate.

It is revealing to look at the reactivity series

from this point of view. Here are some approximate dates for the isolation of half-a-dozen metals. How do they fit in with the position of the metals in the series?

B.C.
5000 Gold, silver and copper in use—no smelting required.
3500 Copper, silver and lead obtained by smelting ores.
2600 Iron known in Egypt.
A.D.
1749 Zinc in use.
1807 Sodium and potassium isolated on laboratory scale.
1886 Aluminium prepared on large scale.
1937 Magnesium obtained from sea water on large scale.

7.5. Carbonates and Heat

Last year you investigated the action of heat on a few metal carbonates, testing with lime water any gas which was driven off (Figure 34).

Now you should do the same with a wider variety of carbonates with a view to finding which decompose with only gentle heating, which require stronger heating and which, if any, do not appear to decompose at all.

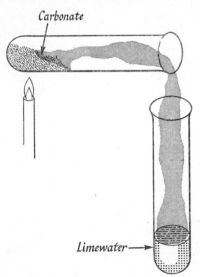

Figure 34

Once you have done this, try to see if there is any connection between this property and the position of the metal in the reactivity series. Here is something else which the knowledgeable chemist can predict. Can you suggest a possible reason why no silver carbonate or mercury carbonate have been found in the earth?

7.6. Electrons changing over

There is one other most important prediction which can be made from the reactivity series.

Do you remember in Form I making needle-shaped crystals of silver using a beaker of silver nitrate solution and a cloth bag containing a little mercury? Is mercury above or below silver in the reactivity series? Perhaps one metal is able to push another, lower in the series, out of its salts? Here is an experiment you can try using a variety of metals.

Cut a small piece of each of the following metal foils—magnesium, copper, silver, zinc, lead and iron. The pieces should be about one-tenth of an inch square. Place one sample of each metal in a hollow of a white dimple tile (Figure 35).

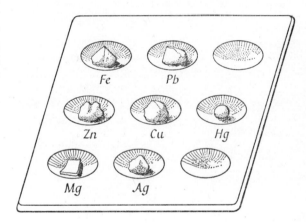

Figure 35

Using a teat pipette cover each metal with a few drops of a solution of silver nitrate. Wait about two minutes before noting which metals have become discoloured.

Wash the tile and repeat the experiment, this time covering each metal with a few drops of a solution of lead (II) nitrate. Again note which metals have become discoloured.

Repeat the experiment using fresh samples of the metals and solutions of copper (II) sulphate, iron (II) sulphate, zinc sulphate and magnesium sulphate.

You can keep your results in a table like Table 1. Enter a tick ($\sqrt{}$) if you notice any discoloration and a cross (x) if nothing seems to happen.

When you have used all the solutions, list the six metals, beginning with the one which had the most ticks and ending with the one with most crosses. How does this list compare with the reactivity series?

Can you suggest what caused the discolorations? Perhaps a look at a piece of zinc foil or an iron knife blade after it has been dipped into copper (II) sulphate solution will help.

Table 1

Metal	Solutions						
	$Ag^+NO_3^-$	$Hg^+NO_3^-$	$Cu^{2+}SO_4^{2-}$	$Pb^{2+}(NO_3)_2^-$	$Fe^{2+}SO_4^{2-}$	$Zn^{2+}SO_4^{2-}$	$Mg^{2+}SO_4^{2-}$
Mg							
Zn							
Fe							
Pb							
Cu							
Hg							
Ag							

Now you have discovered another very important property of metals which can be predicted from the position of the metal in the reactivity series.

Let us work out the equation for one of these reactions—the displacement of silver by copper. We started with:

$$Cu \quad + \quad Ag^+$$
some copper metal   silver ions in an aqueous solution of silver nitrate

and finished with:

$$Ag \quad + \quad Cu^{2+}$$
some silver crystals   copper (II) ions in solution

The complete equation therefore is:

$$Cu + Ag^+ \rightarrow Ag + Cu^{2+}$$

Now we shall try to balance the equation from the point of view of the electrons taking part.

Each copper atom has lost two electrons to become a copper (II) ion, Cu^{2+}. This change is called oxidation (de-electronation). Each silver ion, Ag^+, has been forced to gain one electron to become a silver atom. This change is called reduction (electronation) (3.3, p. 10). It follows therefore that two silver ions, $2Ag^+$, will gain two electrons to become two silver atoms.

$$Cu + 2Ag^+ \rightarrow 2Ag + Cu^{2+}$$

The ability of a metal to force another metal out of its compounds is often referred to as the **displacement** of one metal by another. You might like to carry out another quite spectacular displacement reaction before we leave the topic. Have you ever seen a real silver Christmas tree? Here is how you can make one!

Cut a piece of copper foil to look like a Christmas tree (Figure 36) and suspend it in a beaker of silver nitrate solution. Be careful not to get any

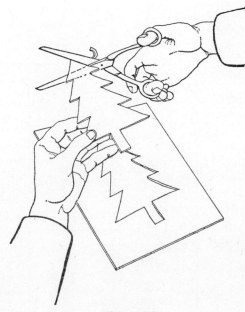

Figure 36

of the solution on your fingers because it will stain them badly. Place the apparatus in the dark and after an hour or two take it out and shine a light on the tree. Can you understand why you now have a silver coating on the copper tree? Can you suggest any other metals which you could have used instead of copper?

This displacement of one metal by another does not take place only in solution. It will also happen in the solid state. Do you remember last year igniting a mixture of copper (II) oxide and powdered zinc? Can you see why we used zinc? A similar experiment can be done with aluminium powder and iron (III) oxide. These reactions give some indication of the energy involved in the transfer of electrons and formation of new compounds.

Summarising the reactivity series

Now that we have established firmly the fact that there is a reactivity series of metals in chemistry, perhaps some of you are asking, 'Why should there be such a series?' You must understand that a piece of metal shows no reactivity until it meets another chemical substance. In most of the cases encountered in this chapter, the basic reaction has been the formation of metal ions from metal atoms or the reverse.

$$M \rightarrow M^+ + \text{electron}$$
$$\text{or } M^+ + \text{electron} \rightarrow M.$$

Why should some metals do this more easily than others? We shall try to answer this question in the next chapter.

Metal					Dates	
Potassium	Metals which displace hydrogen from cold water	Metals too reactive to risk in acid	Carbonates not decomposed by heat	Metals which cannot be obtained from metal oxides using hydrogen	A.D. 1807	In general each metal can displace any metal below it in the list from one of its compounds
Sodium					A.D. 1807	
Lithium						
Calcium						
Magnesium		Metals which displace hydrogen from acid			A.D. 1937	
Aluminium	Metals which displace hydrogen from steam		Carbonates decomposed to give metal oxide and carbon dioxide		A.D. 1886	
Zinc					A.D. 1749	
Iron				Metals which can be obtained from metal oxides using hydrogen	B.C. 2600	
Tin						
Lead						
Hydrogen	Metals which do not displace hydrogen from water or from steam				B.C. 3500	
Copper		Metals which do not displace hydrogen from acid				
Mercury			Carbonates, if any, decompose to give metal oxygen and carbon dioxide	Metals which can be obtained from metal oxides by heat alone		
Silver					B.C. 5000	
Gold					B.C. 5000	
Platinum						

LOOKING BACK AT CHAPTER 7

Before you leave this chapter, you should *know* and *understand* the meaning of the following:
1. Reactivity Series.
2. Displacement.
3. Reduction (electronation).
4. Oxidation (de-electronation).

Something to do

On a copy of the Periodic Table—not the one at the front of this book—

(a) Star in *red* the metals known to the Romans. (Your Latin should help you).

(b) Star in *green* the metals discovered in the Middle Ages.

(c) Star in *blue* the metals discovered from then till the 19th century.

(d) Star in *yellow* the metals used for the first time this century.

Some library research will be necessary to do this job well.

WHY 8 PATTERN IN REACTIVITY?

8.1.

In 1.5 you learned that as you read down the left-hand columns of the Periodic Table, the nuclear charge and the atomic volume of the elements both increase. As you read across the table toward the non-metals on the right-hand side, the nuclear charge again increases, but there is a decrease in atomic volume. Look at Figure 37 which has been taken from Figure 6, p. 4.

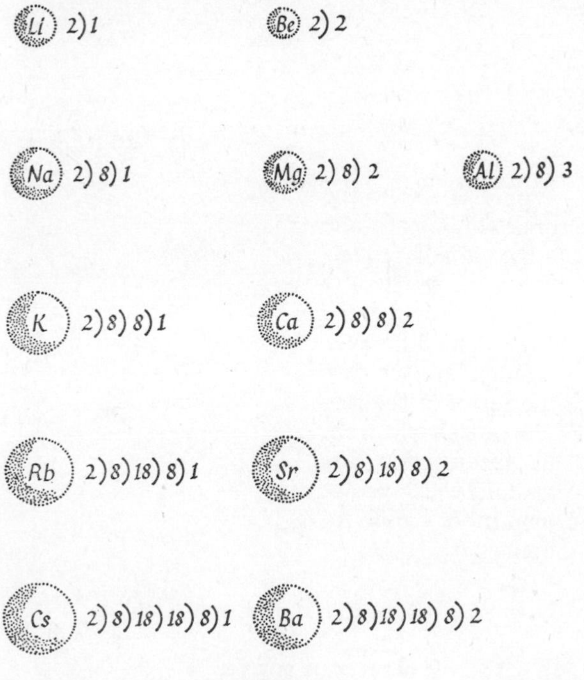

Li 2)1   Be 2)2

Na 2)8)1   Mg 2)8)2   Al 2)8)3

K 2)8)8)1   Ca 2)8)8)2

Rb 2)8)18)8)1   Sr 2)8)18)8)2

Cs 2)8)18)18)8)1   Ba 2)8)18)18)8)2

Figure 37

Nuclear charge and atomic volume are both concerned in the ability of a metal atom to form an ion. Consider the case of the metals lithium, sodium and potassium. Look at the atomic structure of each. As you read from lithium to potassium the positive charge on the nucleus increases. In the case of potassium, which has the largest atomic volume, the outermost electron is further from the nucleus. Despite the larger nuclear charge, this electron is so far away from the nucleus that it is less difficult to remove it than is the case with either sodium or lithium. Potassium is, therefore, the most reactive of these three metals.

The elements in this group of the Periodic Table are called the Alkali Metals. Can you suggest why this name has been given to them? Which is likely to be the most reactive metal in the group?

When the possible reactivity of a metal is being decided, another factor has to be considered. This is the number of electrons which has to be shed from an atom. It seems likely that it will be easier for an atom to lose one electron than to lose two, or for another to shed two rather than three. The energy required to remove three electrons from an atom is so great that you will rarely meet metal ions with a charge of more than $+3$.

To form a mole of Al^{3+} ions from a mole of aluminium atoms (27 g—a small handful) would require a large amount of energy—enough to bring six kettles of water to the boil!

Reading across the Periodic Table from left to right you meet the metals sodium, magnesium and aluminium. This is also their order in the reactivity series. A sodium atom has to lose one electron to become an ion, a magnesium atom two, while an aluminium atom has to lose three. Aluminium, therefore, is the least reactive of the trio.

There are at least three factors which have to be considered when we are deciding how difficult it is for a metallic atom to become a positively charged ion. These are:

(i) the nuclear charge,
(ii) the atomic volume, and
(iii) the number of electrons to be shed.

It must be admitted that this is not quite the whole story, otherwise a metal like iron, which forms iron (II) ions would be expected to be more reactive than aluminium which forms aluminium (III) ions, and this is not the case. Other factors are involved although they cannot be dealt with at this stage. It can be seen, however, that the reasons for the reactivity pattern in the reactions of metals lie to some extent in atomic structure.

8.2. Ionic volumes

Figure 6 gave you an indication of the relative volumes of atoms. Here is an interesting experiment which gives you information concerning the relative volumes of **ions**.

Crystals of the chlorides of lithium, sodium and potassium each contain chloride ions and the respective metal ions, packed in exactly the same way (Figure 38).

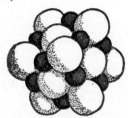

Figure 38

Calculate the formula weight of each compound.

Grind the crystals in a mortar until the size of the grains is about the same. Then weigh one-tenth of the formula weight of each on to separate pieces of filter paper. Label them. Since the formula weight of each chloride contains the same number of ions, the piles of salt on each filter paper also contain the same number of ions (5.5, p. 21).

Next obtain a piece of glass tubing about 4½ ft long and cut it into three equal lengths. Your teacher will supervise the cutting of the glass if you have not done this before.

Close one end of each tube, fit a short thistle funnel (Figure 39) and carefully tip each of the weighed samples into a different tube. Tap them on the bench until the contents have settled. Are your results like those shown in Figure 40?

Remember that each tube contains the same number of metal ions and chloride ions. Since the

same number of chloride ions is common to all three samples, can you say which metal ion must have the largest volume? Which metal ion has the smallest volume?

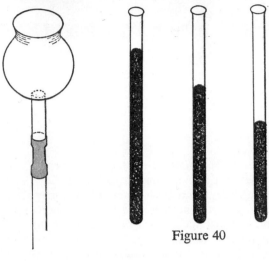

Figure 40

Figure 39

Figure 41 shows the atomic volume of some of the alkali metals together with the corresponding ionic volume. The difference in volume in each case is the result of the loss of the outside electron. This means that the remaining electrons are drawn more closely to the nucleus.

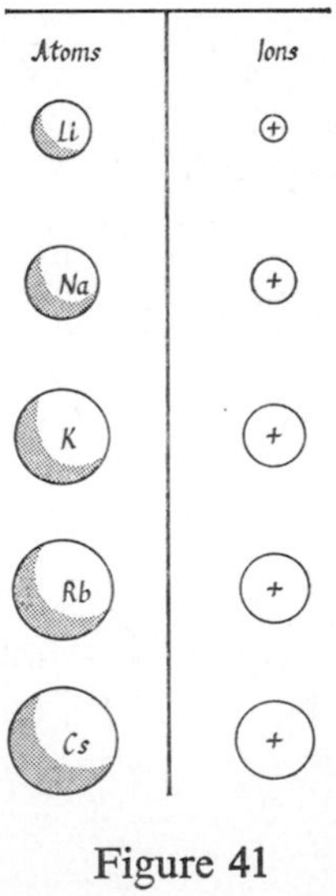

Atoms	Ions
Li	⊕
Na	+
K	+
Rb	+
Cs	+

Figure 41

8.3. Seeing electrons move

When any metal is placed in water it tends to form ions. When a zinc strip, for example, is placed in water some zinc atoms lose electrons and form zinc ions which pass into solution. The electrons left behind pile up on the strip. The valency number of zinc is 2, so we can write

$$Zn \rightarrow Zn^{2+}(aq) + 2e$$

to represent the change.

When a copper strip is placed in water, some copper (II) ions are formed in solution and the electrons again pile up on the strip.

$$Cu \rightarrow Cu^{2+}(aq) + 2e$$

Each metal, however, does not form ions equally readily. In the above examples zinc forms ions more readily than copper. This means that the build-up of electrons on the zinc strip is greater than the build-up on the copper (Figure 42). There will be a greater 'electrical pressure' on the zinc strip than on the copper one because of the greater number of electrons present.

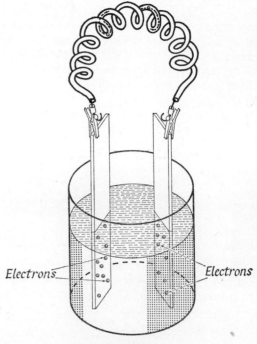

Figure 43

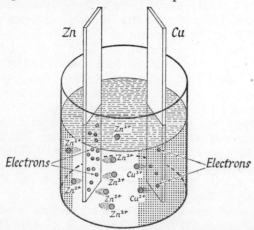

Figure 42

If the two strips are connected with a wire, the electrons on the zinc strip will travel along the wire in an attempt to 'even out' the electrical pressure (Figure 43).

This flow of electrons takes place whenever a wire joins two regions of different electrical pressure. Electrons flow from the region of higher pressure to that of the lower. If a voltmeter is placed in the wire (Figure 44) the flow of electrons causes the pointer to move. The region of higher electrical pressure should be connected to the negative end of the meter.

The extent of the deflection gives some idea of the difference in electrical pressure (or voltage) between the two metals when they are placed in water. If we couple one metal with others in turn and note the reading obtained in each case, we shall be able to compare the ability of metals to form ions in water.

We shall take copper as our standard metal, and the simplest way to make the comparison is

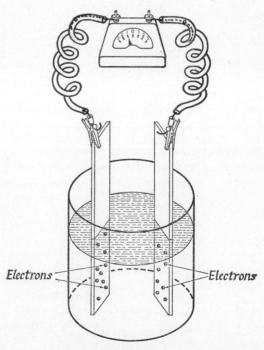

Figure 44

to place a piece of wet filter paper on top of some copper foil. This should be attached by means of a crocodile clip and wire to the positive terminal (red) of a voltmeter. Attach a piece of clean magnesium to the negative (black) terminal in the same way and press it against the copper with the wet filter paper between (Figure 45).

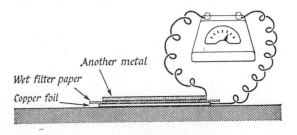

Another metal

Wet filter paper

Copper foil

Figure 45

Is there any reading on the voltmeter?

You can repeat the experiment with any metal which is below magnesium in the reactivity series. Keep a note of the voltages produced as shown in Table 2.

Table 2

Metal	Meter reading

To extend your readings your teacher will show you how fresh samples of more reactive metals can be dealt with. You should not attempt these experiments yourselves.

Now arrange your readings in order of decreasing voltage produced. How does this list of metals compare with the reactivity series?

If you have not already used a metal below copper in the reactivity series perhaps you could predict what would happen. If your teacher has some platinum or silver foil you might be able to test your prediction.

8.4. Electricity from chemicals

In the previous section we discovered that when a metal is placed in water there is a tendency for metal ions to pass into solution and electrons are left behind on the metal.

If two different metals are placed in water, the tendency of each to produce ions is different. This means that a different number of electrons will be left behind on the metals. Consequently, when the two are connected, electrons may flow through the wire, in an effort to spread the electrons evenly on both metals. We say that an electric current passes from one metal to the other.

The difference in the electrical pressure on the two metals, or the **voltage** which drives the electrons through the wire, is measured by a **voltmeter.** An arrangement of this kind which produces electricity is called a **cell.** Usually the metals are dipped into an acid rather than into water.

Chemists assign 'voltage numbers' to metals and to hydrogen. Hydrogen, which in solution can give $2H^+ + 2$ electrons, is given a voltage number of zero. If a metal, under the same conditions, forms ions in solution more readily than hydrogen does, its voltage number is positive. If it for msions in solution less readily than hydrogen does, its voltage number is negative.

	Reaction	Voltage Number
Table 3	Mg, which yields $Mg^{2+} + 2e$	$+2.34$
	Zn, which yields $Zn^{2+} + 2e$	$+0.76$
	Fe, which yields $Fe^{2+} + 2e$	$+0.44$
	Pb, which yields $Pb^{2+} + 2e$	$+0.13$
	H_2, which yields $2H^+ + 2e$	0
	Cu, which yields $Cu^{2+} + 2e$	-0.34
	Ag, which yields $Ag^+ + e$	-0.80

Some of these figures are shown in Table 3.

Using these figures we can calculate the voltage which will result in a flow of electrons when the plates of a cell are joined. The higher the figure the 'livelier' the cell.

Suppose, for example, we have a zinc and a copper plate in dilute acid solution. If we subtract the negative voltage number from the positive one we shall obtain the difference in electrical pressure or voltage between the two plates.

Subtracting -0.34 (the voltage number of copper) from $+0.76$ (the voltage number of zinc) we get $0.76-(-0.34)$

$$=0.76+0.34$$
$$=1.10$$

The voltage of this cell will be 1.1 volts.

Can you calculate the voltage which would be produced if the zinc plate is replaced by an iron one?

If, in calculating cell voltages like this, you find that both voltage numbers have the same sign, you must remember to subtract the voltage number of the less reactive metal from that of the more reactive one.

You will understand that the further apart two metals are in the list in Table 3, the higher will be the voltage produced by a cell in which they are present.

8.5. Electricity from chemicals—some useful cells

It is interesting to examine some of the cells in common use today, although we shall not discuss, in detail, the reactions which take place in them when the current flows.

(i) The lead accumulator

This is one of the commonest arrangements for storing electrical energy and is the source of electricity in a car. The cathode, where the electrons leave, is made of lead and the anode, the positively charged plate or electrode, is coated with lead dioxide. These are immersed in a solution of dilute sulphuric acid.

You can make your own lead accumulator with two clean lead plates and some specially diluted sulphuric acid.

First you must coat one of the strips with lead dioxide. (What is the colour of this compound?) This is easily done by passing electricity through the sulphuric acid for about an hour—your teacher will provide you with the correct strength of current. While the electricity is passing through the acid solution, watch closely what is happening at the anode. Is there anything similar taking place at the cathode?

During this part of the experiment you have been using electrical energy to bring about a chemical change. It would seem reasonable that, if the chemical reaction were allowed to go in the opposite direction we should get electrical energy back again.

When the anode has been prepared, connect it and the lead cathode to a torch bulb. Have you succeeded in recovering the electrical energy? This is an important point to remember about all cells—they produce electrical energy from chemical reactions.

(ii) Alkaline accumulators—Nife cells

These are of two basic types.

(a) Those with tubular nickel hydroxide anodes and flat iron cathodes, and

(b) those with flat nickel hydroxide anodes and flat cadmium cathodes. You may have used cells of this type in the physics laboratory.

In both cases the electrodes are placed in a solution of potassium hydroxide.

Steel is used to construct these cells. This gives a rugged portable container which is unaffected by the alkali which it contains. You may have noticed that the terminals of a car battery are liable to corrode. This does not take place with Nife cells, and they have a very long life. (Can you suggest why they are given the name 'Nife'?) An added advantage is that they can withstand extremes of temperature—arctic or tropical.

They are widely used in telecommunications, in railway signalling and in train lighting, because of their long life. Every ship in the British Navy has a Nife battery for one purpose or another.

They can stand idle without deterioration and thus they find a use in the emergency propulsion of trolley buses. The new Hilton Hotel in London uses Nife batteries for its emergency lighting unit and its fire alarm systems.

(iii) Hermetically sealed cells

This type of cell is a development from the initial alkaline accumulators we discussed in the previous section. They consist of nickel hydroxide anodes and cadmium cathodes, again immersed in potassium hydroxide. How to avoid the evolution of gases during their operation was a problem which was successfully overcome during their development.

These cells do not require maintenance and can be used in any position. They are available in various shapes—small buttons, cylinders and rectangles. They are used in equipment such as cordless shavers, clocks, portable radios and tape recorders.

(iv) *Modern Leclanché Cells*

Probably the most common cell in every day use is the ordinary torch battery. It consists of a carbon rod as anode, and a zinc case which is made the cathode. Both are in contact with a paste of ammonium chloride. If you succeed in opening one you will find that it also contains a large amount of black powder. This is manganese dioxide, and its presence prevents a sudden reduction in the flow of current.

A variation of this cell is the layer type which produces a higher voltage. It does so because it contains several single cells stacked on top of each other and connected in series. It is composed of a number of carbon coated zinc electrodes sandwiched between pieces of cardboard which have been soaked in ammonium chloride. One small cell of this type can replace several of the single cells in a portable radio, making the apparatus less heavy to carry.

(v) *The zinc–mercury cell*

During the last war much research was undertaken in an attempt to find a cell which could produce large amounts of electricity and which could be stored in all climates. This type of cell was the result.

The cathode is made of zinc foil or zinc powder while the anode is mercury which is liberated from mercury (II) oxide during the operation of the cell. The electrodes are immersed in concentrated potassium hydroxide which contains some zinc oxide.

This type of cell has proved to be capable of extreme miniaturisation. The smallest ever produced measures only 0·135 in. by 0·305 in. diameter and weighs 0·02 oz! Thus it finds a use in hearing aids, and in tiny transmitters such as those in 'radio pills'. These radio pills are swallowed by patients, and as they pass through the body they transmit information about the pressure, temperature and acidity or alkalinity inside the body.

Another advance in medical science uses small powerful cells of this type in a device known as the Pacemaker. It is used in cases where the heart beat of a patient is well below the normal value. The 'equipment' is stitched inside the body, with electrodes planted in the heart. Its function is to make the heart beat at the normal rate. For this application the cells must be utterly reliable and, obviously, must have a long life! A minor operation is needed to change the batteries, but this is necessary only every five years.

This is an example of how progress in one branch of science can accelerate progress in another. Whatever happens in the future, the chemist has a vital part to play in the production of packaged electricity.

LOOKING BACK AT CHAPTER 8

Before you leave this chapter, you should *know* and *understand* the meaning of the following:
1. The Alkali Metals.
2. Electrical pressure (or voltage).
3. A Cell.

Something to think about

1. If you had one-tenth of the formula weight of rubidium and caesium chlorides contained in tubes similar to those used in Figure 40, how do you think their heights would compare with those shown?
2. In what sense is the charging and discharging of a cell like the winding up and running down of a clockwork motor? Can energy be created or is it merely converted from one form to another?

THE BATTLE AGAINST CORROSION

As we saw in the previous chapter, uncombined metals, in the presence of water, tend to shed electrons and change to metal ions. They undergo oxidation (or de-electronation). During this process a loss of metal results. The general term applied to this change is **corrosion** and, in the special case of iron, it is called rusting.

When you really think about it, corrosion is the natural behaviour of metals. When left, they revert to their original combined state as compounds, in much the same way as a garden when left unattended reverts 'to the wild'.

Let us look more closely at what takes place when metals are arranged in pairs.

9.1. Metals in pairs

Here is an experiment you can set up in which you can follow the corrosion that takes place when a piece of iron is coupled with various other metals in turn.

Find four shiny iron nails and to each attach a piece of a different metal, such as magnesium, copper, tin and zinc (Figure 46).

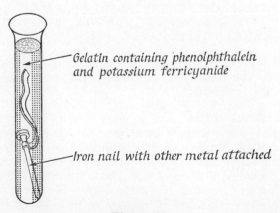
Gelatin containing phenolphthalein and potassium ferricyanide

Iron nail with other metal attached

Figure 46

Put each of these pairs of metals in a test-tube.

Now make about 100 ml of a hot 5% solution of gelatin in water (5 g gelatin dissolved in 100 ml of hot water). Add a small crystal of potassium ferricyanide and two drops of the indicator phenolphthalein. The former gives a blue colour with iron (II) ions and so is a rust detector. The indicator detects alkalis by turning pink.

Cover each pair of metals with the gelatin solution (Figure 46). Cool the test-tubes in cold water and allow them to stand until next chemistry day.

Can you arrange the test-tubes in order, beginning with the one in which the iron has rusted most? This will be the test-tube in which the blue colour is most obvious.

In which test-tubes can you see a pink colour indicating the presence of alkali?

Now we have to explain these results on the basis of our observations in 8.3, p. 34.

What happened when iron was connected to a metal higher in the reactivity series (magnesium) and placed in the gelatin solution? Did much rust form round the nail in this test-tube?

The change $Mg \rightarrow Mg^{2+}(aq) + 2e$, in which magnesium loses electrons, takes place more readily than $Fe \rightarrow Fe^{2+}(aq) + 2e$, in which iron loses electrons. There is therefore a greater number of electrons on the magnesium than on the iron. This means that a negative charge flows to the iron from the magnesium. This prevents the iron from rusting by making the change Fe to $Fe^{2+}(aq) + 2e$ more difficult. But it speeds up the change from Mg to $Mg^{2+}(aq) + 2e$ because electrons are constantly being lost from the magnesium.

The pink colour which has formed in the test-tube containing the iron and magnesium pair shows that magnesium has corroded and alkaline conditions have developed. Let us discuss this change.

(i) $Mg \rightarrow Mg^{2+}(aq) + 2e$

These electrons tend to travel to the iron and some are snapped up by the hydrogen ions present in the water.

(ii) $H^+(aq) + e \rightarrow H$

The hydrogen atoms collect in pairs forming hydrogen gas.

(iii) $H + H \rightarrow H_2$

You may see bubbles of hydrogen gas trying to escape from the gelatin.

As we shall discuss in the next chapter, only a few H^+ and exactly the same number of OH^- are present in water.

$$H_2O \rightarrow H^+ + OH^-$$

Since hydrogen ions cause acid conditions and hydroxyl ions alkaline, the same amount of acidity and alkalinity is present in water. We say that it is neutral.

If many H^+ are removed it means that there will be an excess of OH^- left in the solution. The build up of these ions gives the alkaline conditions which cause the pink colour.

This particular experiment has some important practical applications. One way in which underground iron pipelines are protected is by burying bags containing magnesium turnings near them at intervals of about one furlong. The magnesium is attached to the pipeline by a conductor (Figure 47).

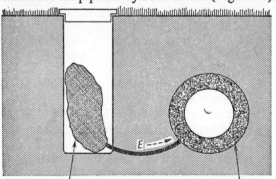

Bag of magnesium scrap   Iron pipeline

Figure 47

The magnesium corrodes and electrons flow to the iron thus making it more difficult for iron (II) ions to form. The magnesium in time is destroyed and the known locations of the magnesium bags are checked periodically and replaced when necessary.

Can you suggest another metal which would prevent the rusting of iron in the same way? Is your answer in agreement with what you see in one of the other test-tubes?

This method of preventing corrosion is referred to as 'cathodic protection' because of the negative charge (cathode—) forced on to the iron. The steel plates of ships and the bodies of motor cars can be protected by bolting blocks of magnesium to them. These corrode preferentially and can easily be replaced while the iron remains almost untouched.

Look again at the test-tubes which contain the iron-copper pair and the iron-tin pair. Do you agree that in these cases the iron has corroded quickly? Both of these metals are below iron in the reactivity series. Which metal is protecting which in these cases? The pattern still fits.

Most of you will know that tin cans, in which food is commonly preserved, are actually made of iron and have only a thin coating of the much more expensive tin. But think of what happens when the thin tin coating is broken by a scratch. The iron, being more reactive than tin, starts to corrode and protects the tin! The rust spreads rapidly as a result and the iron is actually worse off than if the tin coating was not there!

9.2. The rusting of iron

Set up the arrangement shown in Figure 48. Connect the left-hand strip to the negative terminal of the meter.

Is there any reading on the meter?

Add a few drops of bench hydrochloric acid to the left-hand compartment (Figure 49).

Is there any movement on the meter?

We have added more hydrogen ions to the water surrounding the left-hand strip and so the electrons produced by the change

$$Fe \rightarrow Fe^{2+} + 2e$$

are being snapped up more quickly by the hydrogen ions. This time you can probably see bubbles of hydrogen escaping. Corrosion is evidently speeded up by the presence of acids.

You can try the same experiment using strips of other metals. Do any appear to corrode more quickly than iron?

Metal corrosion is a most serious problem. Rain water usually contains acids by dissolving carbon dioxide and other industrial gases in the air. It has been estimated that over one-fifth of the annual production of iron goes to replace the iron lost by corrosion. Not surprisingly, chemists have given a great deal of thought to methods of reducing this loss.

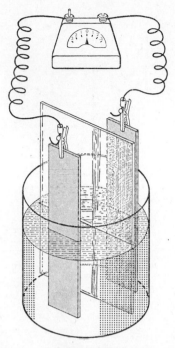

Figure 48

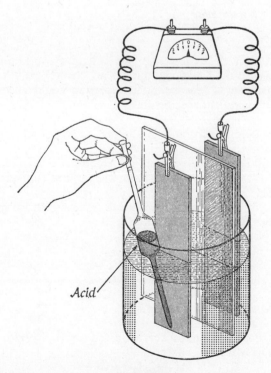

Acid

Figure 49

9.3. Anodising

Last year we mentioned very briefly the process by which the oxide layer on aluminium can be increased in thickness. If your teacher has the necessary apparatus and solutions you might be able to try some anodising for yourselves. Suppose you want to anodise a square of aluminium. The procedure is shown in the first three steps in Figure 50. Your teacher will give you details of the electrolysis.

This porous layer of oxide absorbs dyes quite easily and nowadays many colours can be applied to anodised aluminium. You might like to try dyeing your sample. Step four (Figure 50) shows you what to do. Special dyes are supplied for the purpose.

9.4. Corrosion in reverse

You now know that when metals go into solution they do so as positively charged metal ions or cations. The process is called oxidation (or de-electronation).

One example of this is $Fe \rightarrow Fe^{2+} + 2e$

The reverse process, reduction (or electronation) causes a positively charged metal ion to gain electrons and appear as a recognisable metal.

One example of this is $Cu^{2+} + 2e \rightarrow Cu$

We obtained some metals from their compounds using the method of electrolysis in Form I. These experiments were referred to in 3.3, p. 9.

During electrolysis cations are being persuaded to accept electrons back again and so become neutral atoms. They receive these electrons at the negatively charged electrode or cathode. The ease with which they undergo this reduction is in the order of the reactivity series *backwards*.

Copper will appear more easily than hydrogen and hydrogen more easily than all the metals above it. This explains why, during the electrolysis of the various salt solutions, the only metals you obtained were silver, mercury and copper—all below hydrogen in the reactivity series. In all other cases hydrogen was liberated at the cathode.

We have pointed out that corrosion is the natural process. This reverse change is the unnatural one. Once in solution, cations have to be dragged back, beginning with the least reluctant— the ones at the bottom of the reactivity series. These are the metals which were most reluctant to corrode in the first place.

But we must also think about what happens to anions at the anode during electrolysis. They too

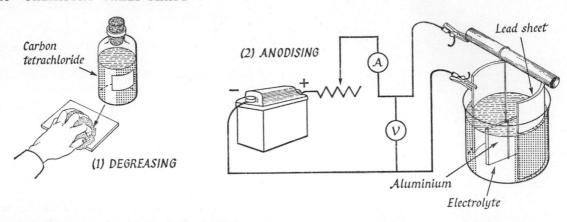

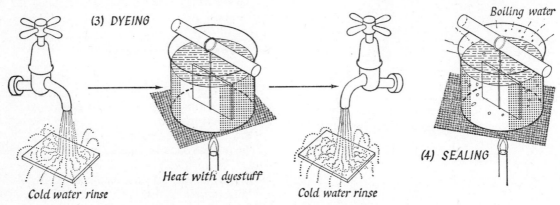

Figure 50

are discharged in a definite order. They lose electrons, that is, they undergo oxidation (or de-electronation) at the positively charged anode.

The order in which anions are discharged in your experiments is—

(i) I^- The change here is from $I^-{\rightarrow}I+e$
(ii) Br^- The change here is from $Br^-{\rightarrow}Br+e$
(iii) Cl^- The change here is from $Cl^-{\rightarrow}Cl+e$
(iv) OH^- The change here is from
$$4OH^-{\rightarrow}2H_2O+O_2+4e$$
Other anions such as SO_4^{2-}, NO_3^- and F^- are not normally discharged in aqueous solutions.

In (iv) each of the four hydroxyl ions loses an electron and the four hydroxide groups left combine to form two molecules of water and one molecule of oxygen. The result is the appearance of oxygen at the anode.

As far as the first three ions are concerned it is the largest one which loses its extra electron most easily because this electron is furthest from the nucleus and therefore not so strongly held. Next year we shall have more to say about this important group of elements.

With this knowledge we can now work out what would happen during an electrolysis. We shall try a few examples and you could check your results experimentally.

A. *The electrolysis of copper sulphate solution between carbon electrodes.*

What ions have we in the solution?

(i) Cu^{2+} and SO_4^{2-} from the copper sulphate, and

(ii) a few hydrogen ions, H^+ and hydroxyl ions, OH^- from the water.

On electrolysis:—

(a) At the cathode.

Since copper is below hydrogen in the reactivity series

$$Cu^{2+}+2e{\rightarrow}Cu$$

i.e. copper is deposited.

(b) At the anode.

Bearing in mind the list given above, hydroxyl ions will be discharged,

$$4OH^-{\rightarrow}2H_2O+O_2+4e$$

i.e. oxygen is liberated.

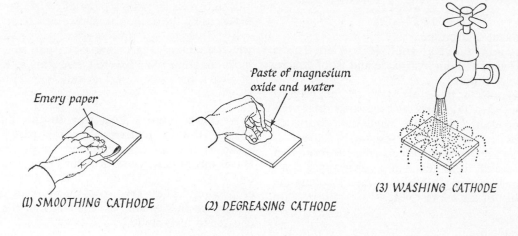

Emery paper

Paste of magnesium
oxide and water

(1) SMOOTHING CATHODE   *(2) DEGREASING CATHODE*   *(3) WASHING CATHODE*

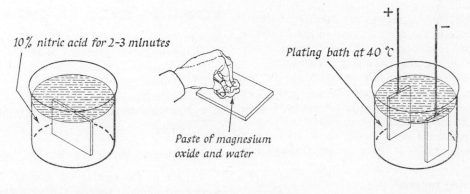

10% nitric acid for 2-3 minutes

Paste of magnesium
oxide and water

Plating bath at 40 °C

(4) ETCHING CATHODE   *(5) DEGREASING ANODE*   *(6) PLATING*

Figure 51

This means that H^+ and SO_4^{2-} will be left in solution.
i.e. sulphuric acid will be formed.

B. *The electrolysis of sulphuric acid solution between carbon or platinum electrodes.*
What ions have we in the solution?
(i) H^+ and SO_4^{2-} from the sulphuric acid when it dissolves, and
(ii) a few H^+ and OH^- from the water.
On electrolysis:—
(a) At the cathode.
Hydrogen ions must be discharged.
$$H^+ + e \rightarrow H$$
Then
$$H + H \rightarrow H_2$$
i.e. hydrogen is liberated.
(b) At the anode.
Hydroxyl ions will be discharged.
$$4OH^- \rightarrow 2H_2O + O_2 + 4e$$
i.e. oxygen is liberated.
In fact water is being removed and an in-creasingly concentrated solution of sulphuric acid will remain.

This is exactly the process which takes place during anodising but the oxygen combines with the aluminium anode to give a thicker layer of aluminium oxide (9.3, p. 39).

C. *The electrolysis of an aqueous solution of sodium chloride.*
What ions have we in the solution?
(i) Na^+ and Cl^- from the sodium chloride, and
(ii) a few H^+ and OH^- from the water.
On electrolysis:—
(a) At the cathode.
Hydrogen will be discharged because hydrogen is below sodium in the reactivity series.
$$H^+ + e \rightarrow H$$
Then
$$H + H \rightarrow H_2$$
i.e. hydrogen is liberated.
(b) At the anode.
Chlorine ions will be discharged.

$$Cl^- \rightarrow Cl + e$$

Then $\quad\quad Cl + Cl \rightarrow Cl_2$

i.e. chlorine is liberated.

This means that Na^+ and OH^- are left. This is a solution of sodium hydroxide and is, of course, alkaline to litmus.

If there is a trace of Mg^{2+} in the original solution, then there will also be some Mg^{2+} left after the electrolysis. Since magnesium hydroxide is much less soluble than sodium hydroxide, it settles as a precipitate. This explains the formation of the cloudy precipitate of a magnesium compound which you investigated when studying the chemistry of the sea last year.

Summarising

1. On electrolysis cations are discharged at the cathode in the reverse order of the reactivity series. Hydrogen is obtained more easily than the metals above it in the series.
2. To obtain metals above hydrogen in the series by electrolysis, water usually must be absent. The electrolysis has to be conducted on the molten salt (3.4, p. 10).
3. In practice, anions are discharged in a definite order—I^-, Br^-, Cl^- and finally OH^-.

9.5. Plating metals

This process involves the covering of one metal with a tough hard coat of another which is slow to corrode. Thus the metal underneath is protected. The plating is carried out by electrolysis under controlled conditions and the metal is often chosen for its attractive appearance as well as for its slow rate of corrosion.

You can easily plate a piece of copper foil with nickel using the apparatus shown in Figure 51.

Your teacher will give you the plating solution which contains nickel ions, Ni^{2+}, and you must make the piece of copper foil the cathode. A piece of nickel, such as a nickel spatula, will do for the anode.

We have come a long way in this difficult chapter toward understanding the part which electrons play in corrosion and its prevention. Have you noticed how frequently the hydrogen ion, $H^+(aq)$, and the hydroxyl ion, $OH^-(aq)$, have cropped up? These are two of the most important ions in chemistry and we shall devote the next chapter to their study.

LOOKING BACK AT CHAPTER 9

Before you leave this chapter, you should *know* and *understand* the meaning of the following:

1. Corrosion.
2. Cathodic protection.
3. Anodising.
4. Electrolysis—Corrosion in reverse.
5. Plating.

Something to think about

1. Earlier in the course we noticed that metals were crystalline. If we crack the crystals by bending a nail, what effect does this have on the rate of corrosion? The jelly experiments (9.1, p. 37) will help you to investigate this. Be sure to compare the bent nail with a straight one.
2. Why did the Romans completely cover iron nails with copper before using them to nail copper sheathing on to the bottom of wooden ships?

TWO **10** IMPORTANT IONS

In Chapter 5.2 we mentioned that all acids are compounds of hydrogen. But not all hydrogen compounds are acids! This is the same kind of statement as 'all boys are human beings, but not all human beings are boys'.

The hydrogen compounds which are acids are those which yield **hydrogen ions** when they are dissolved in water.

Acids are not all poisonous or corrosive. Many of our foods are acid, our drinking water is acid and many of the liquids in our digestive system are acids. What makes a compound an acid is that it can release hydrogen ions to other substances with which it comes in contact.

10.1. The hydrogen ion

Let us remind ourselves of the structure of the hydrogen atom (^1_1H). It has one proton in its nucleus and one electron moving round it. A hydrogen ion forms when this atom gives its electron to another atom. In other words a hydrogen ion is a **proton**—an intensely positively charged scrap of material. It is unlikely that such an object could exist on its own. It has to find something negative to attach itself to. This could be a negative ion or even the negative end of a polar molecule such as water. We meet most acids dissolved in water and so the hydrogen ion (the proton) will be attached to one or more water molecules. During the manufacture of hydrochloric acid, hydrogen chloride gas is passed into water. Something like this must happen.

$$H \overset{\delta+}{—} O \overset{\delta-}{} + H \overset{\delta+}{—} Cl \overset{\delta-}{} \rightarrow H_3O^+ + Cl^-$$
$$\underset{H}{\overset{\delta+}{\diagdown}}$$

The water molecules will attract the hydrogen atom on the hydrogen chloride molecule. Since the hydrogen chloride molecule is polar, the hydrogen atom already has a slightly positive charge and it will be pulled from the chlorine atom on to the water molecule.

Of course water molecules will cluster round all kinds of ions and we say that such ions are hydrated. You may remember that this is some-times denoted as (aq). And so when the hydrogen ion is in water we shall write it H^+(aq). Some books represent the hydrogen ion throughout as H_3O^+, but this is not more correct than H^+(aq).

We shall, therefore, define an acid as a substance which can yield protons (H^+) to other substances.

10.2. The behaviour of the hydrogen ion

In the first year you identified acids by their effect on a dye called litmus. It is the hydrogen ion which causes this effect. Litmus is a simple and not very sensitive indicator. There are some interesting indicators called 'wide range' or 'universal' indicators which have as many as a dozen possible colour changes. These indicators not only tell us if a substance is an acid, but also tell us the H^+ concentration.

Here is an experiment you can do to find out how concentration and colour change are related.

You will be supplied with a solution which contains the formula weight in grams of hydrogen chloride in each litre. Such a solution, called a **molar solution,** is usually denoted by M.

We are going to dilute this solution and see its effect on the universal indicator.

This is a simple experiment, but you must do it fairly carefully to get reasonable results.

Take 10 ml of the molar (M) solution and dilute it to 100 ml with distilled water. Shake this solution well. We now have an M/10 solution. Fill a clean dry test-tube with it, label it M/10 and set it aside in a rack for testing later.

Take another 10 ml of the M/10 solution and dilute it to 100 ml with distilled water. Mix well. We now have an M/100 solution. Set aside a test-tube full of it. Take 10 ml of the M/100 solution and dilute it once more to 100 ml with distilled water. This will give an M/1000 solution.

Keep doing this diluting until you have a M/10,000,000 solution. Your measuring cylinders should be carefully rinsed with distilled water between each dilution.

You should now have seven test-tubes of solution ranging in concentration from M 10 to M/10,000,000. Dip a piece of universal indicator paper into each test-tube and then quickly compare the colour with the colours on the packet. Each colour has a number. Write down the number corresponding to the dilution in each tube. A Table like this will do.

And so at pH 7 the number of hydrogen ions and hydroxyl ions must be the same, that is, 10^{-7} mole/1litre.

This is a very important scale biologically. Many body fluids will operate satisfactorily only if the pH is of a certain value (Figure 52).

Certain plants will grow well only in soil of quite definite pH values. For example, rhododendrons and azaleas grow in acid soil (pH 5). Other plants require lime (calcium hydroxide) which gives soil with a pH greater than 7.

In gardening shops you can buy pH paper for

Table 4

Dilution	M/10	M/100	M/1,000	M/10,000	M/100,000	M/1,000,000	M/10,000,000
Number							

Do you see any connection between the dilution and the number?

The number is the same as the number of nothings on the bottom line of the concentration. These numbers are known as pH numbers and we use them when we are describing acids in which the hydrogen ion concentration is very low.

What is the pH value for distilled water?

This indicates that there must be comparatively few hydrogen ions in pure water. In a litre of pure water there is only one ten-millionth of a gram (10^{-7}g) of hydrogen ion! No wonder it is so difficult to electrolyse distilled water!

On the packet of pH papers you will notice that the pH values go beyond 7. Usually on universal indicators the pH numbers go up to 13.

10.3. The other important ion

A litre of a molar solution of sodium hydroxide will contain a mole of sodium ions and a mole of hydroxyl ions. If this is diluted as the molar acid was in the previous section and tested with the indicator papers, you will find that each dilution will bring you one step down the pH scale until you reach pH 7 once more. Record your results as before.

When a water molecule breaks up it must give one hydroxyl ion for every hydrogen ion.
$$H_2O \rightarrow H^+(aq) + OH^-(aq)$$

soil testing. It enables you to test the pH of your garden soil and then calculate how much lime to add to make the soil suitable for certain plants.

We have learned that the hydrogen ion is what makes a compound an acid. It affects dyes (indicators) and makes them change colour depending upon the concentration of the hydrogen ion.

The hydroxyl ion is common to all alkalis and together with the hydrogen ion it forms water.

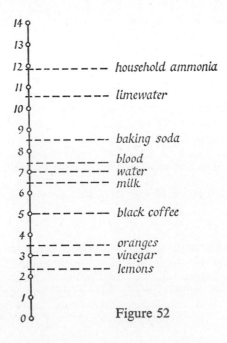

Figure 52

The concentration of these ions is placed on one scale—the pH scale from 1 to 14. When the concentration of hydrogen ions and hydroxyl ions is equal, the pH is 7 because water has been formed.

10.4. Ions are mobile

Here are two experiments you can do to find how fast ions move. Left alone, ions spread out in all directions but when electrodes are placed in the solution the ions move toward the electrodes of the opposite charge (3.3, p. 9).

(a) Make a solution of gelatin in hot water, add a little potassium nitrate and some universal indicator solution until the solution is quite green. Fill two U-tubes to within one inch of the top with the hot gelatin solution and leave it to set.

Set up the two tubes as shown in Figure 53.

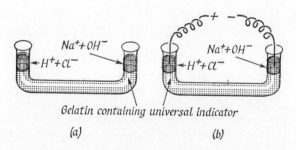

Figure 53

Place molar hydrochloric acid in the left limbs of both and molar sodium hydroxide in the right limbs. In tube (a) as the hydrogen ions and hydroxyl ions diffuse into the gelatin, they will affect the indicator and show coloured bands. In tube (b) we have the same situation, but the hydrogen ions will be attracted round the U by the negative electrode (cathode) and similarly the hydroxyl ions will be attracted to the anode. Their rate of movement will be seen by the coloured bands which appear as they affect the indicator.

How does the rate of movement (the mobility) of the hydrogen ions compare with the hydroxyl ions in tube (a)? Is there a different result in tube (b) when a potential difference has been applied?

(b) You will be provided with molar solutions of hydrochloric acid, sodium chloride and sodium hydroxide. (A litre of each of these solutions contains a mole of cations and a mole of anions.

100 ml of each will therefore contain one tenth of a mole of each ion.)

Using the conductivity apparatus (Figure 15, p. 11), measure the conductivity of 100 ml of M hydrochloric acid. Keeping the sensitivity control steady, measure the conductivity of the other two solutions. How do the three results compare?

Let us compare the results of the hydrochloric acid and the sodium chloride. In both solutions there is one-tenth of a mole of chloride ions and so any difference in conductivity is due to the mobility of one-tenth of a mole of hydrogen ions compared with the mobility of one-tenth of a mole of sodium ions. The results indicate that the hydrogen ions are more mobile than the sodium ions.

A comparison of the sodium chloride and sodium hydroxide solutions will similarly show that the hydroxyl ions are more mobile than the chloride ions.

Experiment (a) above should indicate that the hydrogen ions are about twice as mobile as the hydroxyl ions.

We do not have enough time to investigate the mobility of a large number of ions, but the results can be summed up roughly like this. If the mobility of the hydrogen ion is taken to be 10, then the mobility of the hydroxyl ion is about 5 and that of all other common ions is about 2.

This fact will be very useful to us in the next chapter.

LOOKING BACK AT CHAPTER 10

Before you leave this chapter, you should *know* and *understand* the meaning of the following:
  1. Acids.
  2. Polar hydrogen chloride molecule.
  3. pH Scale.
  4. Molar Solution.
  5. Alkalis.
  6. Mobilities of Ions.

Something to think about

1. Suppose that you were provided with 100 ml of each of M, M/10 and M/100 hydrochloric acid solutions. How would the conductivities of these solutions compare with each other?

2. There are two main factors controlling the conductivity of a solution. From your experiments and your answer to question 1, what would you say these factors were?

HOW NEUTRAL IS NEUTRAL?

11.1.

In the first year, when we mixed acids and alkalis to make salts, we used a piece of litmus paper to tell us when we had added enough acid to neutralise the alkali. Using a burette we added acid to the alkali, a little at a time, until the colour of the litmus just turned from blue to pink. This process is called **titration.** The change in the colour of litmus takes place between pH 8 and pH 5. It begins to change colour while the solution is still alkaline and the change is not complete until the solution is quite acid.

What do we mean by saying that we have neutralised an acid with an alkali? Do we mean that we end up with a solution of pH 7—the same pH as water?

Take a few crystals of each of the following salts and dissolve them in separate test-tubes of distilled water. Test each solution with universal indicator.

From these results you can see that solutions of salts are seldom at pH 7. The neutralisation process gives rise to salts which are not neutral in the sense that water is.

Water is neutral because the number of hydrogen ions and hydroxyl ions are equal.

Why do all salt solutions not have a pH of 7?

11.2.

(a) Let us see what happens when ammonium chloride dissolves in water. To begin with we shall have a mixture of four kinds of ion surrounded by water molecules.

$$NH_4^+ + Cl^- + H^+ + OH^-$$

When a hydrogen ion and a chloride ion meet they will not in any way combine. From our conductivity work (3.5, p. 12) we found that hydrochloric acid was a strong electrolyte. It provided a very large number of ions in solution.

But what happens when ammonium ions and hydroxyl ions meet? Conductivity measurements

Table 5

Salt	pH	Acid	Base
Sodium chloride			
Ammonium chloride			
Sodium acetate			
Potassium nitrate			
Sodium sulphite			
Zinc sulphate			
Iron (III) chloride			

Copy this Table into your notebook.

Under the column marked 'Acid' write the name of the acid from which the salt was formed and, under the heading 'Base', name the hydroxide from which these salts could have been made.

on ammonium hydroxide solution showed that it was a weak electrolyte (3.5, p. 12). This means that only a fairly small number of ammonium ions and hydroxyl ions are present in solution. There is therefore some reaction which tends to remove these ions. A possible reaction is

$$NH_4^+ + OH^- \rightarrow NH_3 + H_2O \text{ (ammonia solution)}.$$

This will reduce the number of free hydroxyl ions leaving an excess of hydrogen ions. The pH cannot be 7. It must be on the acid side.

The salt of a strong (completely ionised) acid and a weak (slightly ionised) base has a pH less than 7.

(b) We have found that sodium acetate solution has a pH greater than 7. Why should this be so?

The acetate ion is a fairly complicated one with the formula $CH_3CO_2^-$.

At first there are four species of ion.

$$Na^+ + CH_3CO_2^- + H^+ + OH^-$$

The sodium ions and hydroxyl ions will not link up in the strong electrolyte sodium hydroxide. However, the hydrogen ion and the acetate ion may very well combine to give the weak acid, acetic acid. Only a small proportion of the molecules of acetic acid are ionised (3.5, p. 12).

$$CH_3CO_2^- + H^+ \rightarrow CH_3CO_2H$$

Since some of the hydrogen ions are 'locked up' in the acetic acid molecules, there will be more hydroxyl ions in solution than hydrogen ions. The solution must be alkaline, with a pH greater than 7.

A salt of a weak acid and a strong base will not have a pH of 7, but will be on the alkaline side with a pH greater than 7.

(c) Salts like sodium chloride which are made from a strong acid and a strong base will have a pH close to 7 because none of the ions in solution has any tendency to link up and upset the equality of the number of hydrogen ions and hydroxyl ions.

This process by which salts react with water to give solutions of pH other than 7 is called **hydrolysis**.

Summary

Solutions of salts of
(a) strong acids and weak bases are acid (pH less than 7)
(b) weak acids and strong bases are alkaline (pH greater than 7)
(c) strong acids and strong bases have pH = 7.

This solid piece of theory now leads us on to some interesting practical work.

11.3. Tailor made indicators

In 11.1, p. 46 we noted that litmus changes colour over a fairly wide pH range. It is useful for indicating if a substance is a definite acid or a definite alkali. But the pH of several salt solutions are outwith the range of litmus and so we must employ other indicators with more definite colour changes over a narrower pH range.

Let us make some salts to get practice in the handling of burettes and pipettes. This is something you cannot learn from a book, but it is a practical skill which is worth developing.

Here are some salts you should try to make; ammonium chloride, potassium nitrate and sodium acetate. There will not be time for everyone to make every salt, but it would be worth while to see the colour change (the end-point) of the various indicators in use.

You will have to decide upon an indicator. This can be done by making a solution of the salt in distilled water and finding its pH. Consult the list of indicators below and decide which is the best one to give a colour change when your salt has just formed. You will also have to decide which acid and base are required to make the salt you choose. Pipette 25 ml of the base into a conical flask, add two drops of the chosen indicator and titrate with the acid until the indicator just changes colour. Note the amount of acid used to the nearest 0·1 ml. Pour away the solution and repeat the titration to confirm the volume of acid used. As your skill improves you should be able to get your results to agree to 0·1 ml (2 drops).

If you want a crystalline specimen of the salt, begin again but do not add any indicator. You now know the volume of acid required to neutralise 25 ml of the base and so you can add this volume directly from the burette. Evaporate the solution to about half volume and transfer it to a warm crystallising dish. Cover it and set it aside for a few days.

Indicators and pH range

Methyl orange pH 3·1 (red) to 4·4 (yellow).
Methyl red pH 4·4 (red) to 6·2 (yellow).
Bromo-thymol blue pH 6·0 (yellow) to 7·6 (blue).
Phenolphthalein pH 8·2 (colourless) to 10·0 (red).

Your teacher may have a selection of other indicators which you can use. Normally the pH range is marked on the label.

If you have to use phenolphthalein you will find it easier to put the acid in the flask and the alkali in the burette. It is easier to detect the appearance of a red tinge than it is to decide when a pale pink has become colourless. It is important to wash the burette thoroughly after it has contained alkali to prevent the tap from cementing solid.

11.4. Find the concentration

Let us remind ourselves of the meaning of the term **molar solution**.

A **molar solution** is one which contains the formula weight in grams of the dissolved substance in one litre of solution.

$$H^+ + Cl^- + Na^+ + OH^- \rightarrow Na^+ + Cl^- + H_2O$$

From this balanced equation you can see that one formula weight of hydrochloric acid would exactly neutralise one formula weight of sodium hydroxide. If both solutions are molar, 1 litre of molar hydrochloric acid would neutralise 1 litre of molar sodium hydroxide. Or any volume (x ml) of molar hydrochloric acid would neutralise the same volume (x ml) of molar sodium hydroxide.

Suppose that in 11.3 you measured out 25 ml molar sodium hydroxide into the conical flask and titrated it with hydrochloric acid of unknown concentration. If you required only 20 ml of acid to neutralise the alkali, the acid solution cannot be molar. What is its concentration? It is very easy to calculate this if you follow this procedure.

$$\underset{\text{1 litre molar}}{Na^+ + OH^-} + \underset{\text{1 litre molar}}{H^+ + Cl^-} \rightarrow Na^+ + Cl^- + H_2O$$

∴ 25 ml M solution of sodium hydroxide should require 25 ml M hydrochloric acid to neutralise it. But 25 ml M solution of sodium hydroxide in practice required 20 ml of the given hydrochloric acid.

∴ Concentration of the acid is $\dfrac{25}{20}$ M = *1·25 M*

The fraction 1·25 is obtained by dividing the volume of acid if it had been molar (i.e. 25 ml) by the actual volume of acid used (i.e. 20 ml).

This next example looks more complicated, but it is just as easy as the one above.

Let us suppose that you were titrating M sodium hydroxide with sulphuric acid of unknown concentration. 25 ml M sodium hydroxide require 15 ml acid to neutralise it.

Write the balanced equation first.

$$\underset{\text{2 litres molar}}{2Na^+ + 2OH^-} + \underset{\text{1 litre molar}}{2H^+ + SO_4^{2-}} \rightarrow 2Na^+ + SO_4^{2-} + 2H_2O$$

∴ 25 ml M sodium hydroxide would require 12·5 ml M sulphuric acid to neutralise it.

But 25 ml M sodium hydroxide in practice require 15 ml sulphuric acid.

∴ Concentration of the acid is $\dfrac{12·5}{15}$ M = *0·8 M*

We have now met a useful method for finding the concentration of acid or alkaline solutions. If you know the concentration of one solution you can use it to find the concentration of any other acid or alkali.

This is a standard method of analysis by which chemists find the concentration of solutions.

We have not yet fully explored the meaning of the term neutralisation and so in the next chapter we shall carry our investigations further.

LOOKING BACK AT CHAPTER 11

Before you leave this chapter, you should *know* and *understand* the meaning of the following:
1. Titration.
2. Hydrolysis.
3. Indicator.
4. Molar solution.

Some calculations to try

20 ml of M sodium hydroxide required (a) 15 ml of hydrochloric acid to neutralise it in one experiment, (b) 20 ml of sulphuric acid to neutralise it in another experiment and (c) 30 ml of nitric acid to neutralise it in a third experiment.

Calculate the concentration of each of these acids.

WHAT IS **12** NEUTRALISATION?

12.1.

We learned in the first year that the process of neutralisation had something to do with making salts. But what really is a salt?

In 5.2, p. 20 it was pointed out that when a salt is formed the parent acid gives its anion to the salt.

All *sulphates* are formed from *sulphuric acid* (hydrogen sulphate solution).

All *chlorides* are formed from *hydrochloric acid* (hydrogen chloride solution).

All *nitrates* are formed from *nitric acid* (hydrogen nitrate solution).

All *phosphates* are formed from *phosphoric acid* (hydrogen phosphate solution).

This could now be extended to include carbonates, sulphites, nitrites, acetates and so on.

However, a salt also contains a cation—either a metal ion or the ammonium ion. What are the possible sources of these cations? Search back into your earlier notes for substances which neutralise acids giving salts.

(a) A fairly obvious source of metal ions would be *metals*. But do all metals react with acids to give salts (7.3, p. 26)?

Here is one which does.

$$Mg + 2H^+ + 2Cl^- \rightarrow Mg^{2+} + 2Cl^- + H_2$$

What other metals could behave similarly?

(b) Earlier in the course we used *basic oxides* to neutralise acids to form salts.

$$Cu^{2+}O^{2-} + 2H^+ + SO_4^{2-} \rightarrow Cu^{2+} + SO_4^{2-} + H_2O$$

This would be a good opportunity to try out a range of basic oxides and acids to see if any general pattern of behaviour appears. Your teacher will provide a selection of oxides and acids for you to investigate.

Remember the procedure. Take two inches of dilute acid in a test-tube and warm it until you can just bear it on the palm of your hand. *Do not boil the acid*. Add the oxide a little at a time until no more will dissolve. Filter off any unused oxide and set the solution aside to crystallise. Record any interesting colour changes. Try to write an ionic equation for each reaction.

(c) Another group of compounds we met earlier react with acids. They are the *carbonates*.

$$Ca^{2+}CO_3^{2-} + 2H^+ + 2Cl^- \rightarrow Ca^{2+} + 2Cl^- + H_2O + CO_2$$

If you have time you could investigate the behaviour of a range of carbonates and acids to see if a pattern emerges. In this case there is no need to warm the acid, but otherwise the method is the same as in (b) above.

(d) The other class of compound which neutralises acids is, of course, the *bases* (the hydroxides). We have discussed the soluble bases (the alkalis) in some detail already.

$$K^+ + OH^- + H^+ + NO_3^- \rightarrow K^+ + NO_3^- + H_2O$$

12.2

Let us now look back over these four methods of neutralisation. What do they all have in common? There is a pattern.

In each case the *hydrogen ions liberated by the acids in solution have been taken away*. When the salt crystallises the metal cations settle with the anions from the acid to form the salt crystal. In the first case the hydrogen ions have been forced to accept electrons and leave the solution as hydrogen gas. This is a displacement reaction.

$$Mg \rightarrow Mg^{2+} + 2e$$
$$2e + 2H^+ \rightarrow H_2$$

The escape of the hydrogen is obvious to the naked eye and the metal seems to vanish into solution.

It is worth while pausing for a moment to remind ourselves that the equations are an expression of the theory. What we know for certain from experiment is that the metal seems to go into solution and hydrogen bubbles appear. An electric current can be shown to be involved (9.2, p. 38) and a salt is formed. The *explanation is theory*, but it is a theory that has been widely accepted because it can forecast and 'explain' the behaviour of many chemical reactions.

In (b), (c) and (d) however, no hydrogen gas is seen to escape. Where have the hydrogen ions gone? The salt obtained from magnesium and hydrochloric acid is exactly the same as that obtained from magnesium oxide and hydrochloric acid. If no hydrogen appears when the oxide is used, where might it have gone? The equation in (b) suggests that it has gone to form water. We have been accepting this until now without question. Is there any experimental evidence for this? The H_2O happens to fit the equation but that may be just a bit of 'juggling' with pencil and paper.

Is there any property of the hydrogen ion that we could use to find if it is being removed? Turn back to 10.4, p. 45.

If the fast moving hydrogen ion is replaced by any other slow moving ion, less current will be carried through the solution and the conductivity of that solution will decrease.

Using the conductivity apparatus (3.5, Figure 15) let us investigate this. Fill the beaker to about two-thirds of its depth with distilled water and add *five drops* of molar sulphuric acid. Adjust the sensitivity control to give a high reading on the meter. The conductivity of the solution is due to hydrogen ions and sulphate ions. Add about a gram of copper (II) oxide powder and stir the solution. Record the meter reading for four consecutive observations. Make a *rough* graph of meter readings against time (Figure 54). There is no need to make a detailed plot because all we are looking for to support our theory is a drop in conductivity to show that the mobile hydrogen ions have been replaced by the slow moving copper (II) ions. Any water formed will have a very low conductivity (10.2, p. 44).

Allow any excess copper (II) oxide powder to settle. Look carefully at the solution. Is there any other evidence for the presence of Cu^{2+}?

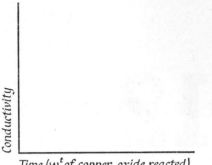

Time (w^t of copper oxide reacted)   Figure 54

12.3.

Similar reasoning can be applied to the reactions in (c) and (d). Conductivity measurements on these reactions may also be of help to us.

Investigate the carbonate-acid reaction in the same way as the basic oxide-acid reaction above. Zinc carbonate or copper (II) carbonate could be used with sulphuric or nitric acid. A *few drops* of molar acid in a beaker of distilled water will be quite sufficient. A rough graph on the same axes as shown above will do.

Do you notice which neutralisation is faster at room temperature—the carbonate-acid type or the basic oxide-acid type?

An investigation of the acid-alkali type of neutralisation is slightly different, but the principle is the same.

Prepare the acid by adding a few drops of molar sulphuric acid to a beaker of distilled water as before. Add a few drops of indicator— almost any indicator will do. Now from a dropper add molar sodium hydroxide, a drop at a time, and stir. Note the meter reading after each drop, but again a very detailed plot of the results is not necessary (Figure 55). We are interested in the *trend* of the conductivity.

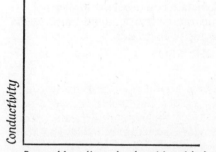

Drops M sodium hydroxide added   Figure 55

Is there any connection between the indicator colour change and the meter readings? Why?

Summary—Some General Equations

We have evidence in each of the four methods of neutralisation for the fact that hydrogen ions from the acid are removed. When the salt is crystallised the metal ions settle into a pattern with the anions from the acid.

In type (a)

mazit metal + acid → salt + *Hydrogen*

(**mazit** stands for Magnesium, Aluminium, Zinc, Iron and Tin)

In type (b)

basic oxide + acid → salt + *Water*

In type (c)

carbonate + acid → salt + carbon dioxide + *Water*

In type (d)

base (hydroxide) + acid → salt + *Water*

In neutralisation, the hydrogen ions released by the acids in solution either collect an electron each and go off as hydrogen gas or go to form water.

The key to most neutralisations seems to be the formation of **water**. Once again, the compound **water** is taking a prominent part in chemical reactions.

12.4.

There is one other interesting piece of evidence which we shall examine before we leave the topic of neutralisation. You can see that a pattern has emerged which links the four methods together.

One of the earliest things we learned about a chemical reaction was that heat is always involved. It is either given out (exothermic reaction) or taken in (endothermic reaction). If, as we have said above, the important reaction in neutralisation is the formation of water, then the heat change involved should be the same in each case if the same weight of water is produced.

$$H^+ + Cl^- \quad + \quad Na^+ + OH^- \rightarrow Na^+ + Cl^- + \quad H_2O$$

1 formula weight	1 formula weight	1 formula weight
∴ 1 litre of molar solution	∴ 1 litre of molar solution	

On both sides of the equation there is a mole of sodium ions and a mole of chloride ions. The only reaction which has taken place is—

$$H^+ + OH^- \rightarrow H_2O$$

Similarly—

$$H^+ + NO_3^- \quad + \quad Na^+ + OH^- \rightarrow Na^+ + NO_3^- + \quad H_2O$$

1 formula weight	1 formula weight	1 formula weight
∴ 1 litre of molar solution	∴ 1 litre of molar solution	

Sodium ions and nitrate ions appear on both sides. Once again the essential reaction would seem to be—

$$H^+ + OH^- \rightarrow H_2O$$

or again—

$$2H^+ + SO_4^{2-} \quad + \quad 2Na^+ + 2OH^- \rightarrow 2Na^+ + SO_4^{2-} + \quad 2H_2O$$

1 formula weight	2 formula weights	2 formula weights
∴ 1 litre of molar solution	∴ 2 litres of molar solution	

∴ 1 litre of molar sulphuric acid + 2 litres of molar sodium hydroxide gives 2 formula weights of water.

∴ ½ litre of molar sulphuric acid + 1 litre of molar sodium hydroxide gives 1 formula weight of water.

$$∴ H^+ + OH^- \rightarrow H_2O$$

There is the theory. Does it stand up to experiment? Does the reaction of a litre of molar hydrochloric acid with a litre of molar sodium hydroxide give the same temperature rise as the reaction of a litre of molar of nitric acid with a litre of molar sodium hydroxide?

Take 10 ml molar hydrochloric acid in one beaker and 10 ml molar sodium hydroxide in another. Find the temperature of each and average them to give the 'original temperature'. Mix the acid and alkali together in a plastic or waxed paper beaker. Measure the highest temperature reached by the mixture. Calculate the temperature change.

Do exactly the same with M nitric acid and M sodium hydroxide. How do the results compare?

To make a fair comparison with sulphuric acid we found that we would need only half as much sulphuric acid as sodium hydroxide if both solutions were molar. But this would only provide 15 (i.e. 5 + 10) ml of solution whereas in the other two we had a total of 20 ml of solution. This can be overcome by using 10 ml M/2 sulphuric acid instead of 5 ml M acid to react with the alkali.

Take 10 ml M/2 sulphuric acid and 10 ml M sodium hydroxide and perform the experiment as before. Other members of the class could do a similar set of experiments using molar potassium hydroxide. How do the results compare? Do not go on *your* results alone, but collect results from other groups in your class. Only an average of a number of determinations is worth examining for the emergence of any pattern.

Has the theory been able to stand up to experiment? Is the formation of water the common essential of most neutralisations?

LOOKING BACK AT CHAPTER 12

Before you leave this chapter, you should *know* and *understand* the meaning of the following:

1. General Equations.
2. Neutralisation—the removal of hydrogen ions.
3. Exothermic Reaction.
4. Endothermic Reaction.

Something to think about

1. Do you think that the process of breaking up molecules of a substance into ions would be exothermic or endothermic?
2. A pupil doing the reactions in 12.4 using molar acetic acid and molar sodium hydroxide, always found that the temperature rise he obtained was lower than that found by his neighbours who were using molar hydrochloric acid. Why?

BOTH **13** SALT AND ACID

13.1.

In Chapter 10, p. 43 we decided that an acid was a substance which could yield hydrogen ions (protons) to other substances.

A litre of a molar solution of hydrochloric acid (H^+Cl^-) would contain a mole of hydrogen ions and a mole of chloride ions. Similarly, a molar solution of nitric acid ($H^+NO_3^-$) would contain a mole of hydrogen ions and a mole of nitrate ions. However, in the case of sulphuric acid ($H_2^+SO_4^{2-}$) there is a different situation. From the formula we should expect to have two moles of hydrogen ions and one mole of sulphate ions per litre of molar acid. It is not quite as simple as this. When very concentrated sulphuric acid is added to water, it releases *one* hydrogen ion from each molecule to join the water molecules. This happens fairly easily.

This means that one hydrogen atom remains attached to the sulphate part to give an ion HSO_4^-, called the *bisulphate ion*.

$$H_2SO_4 \rightarrow H^+ + HSO_4^-$$

The second hydrogen ion can be detached with greater difficulty to give the sulphate ion (SO_4^{2-}) on its own.

$$HSO_4^- \rightarrow H^+ + SO_4^{2-}$$

In other words, the sulphuric acid molecule ionises *in two stages* when it comes in contact with something which will accept the hydrogen ions.

$$H_2SO_4 \rightarrow H^+ + HSO_4^- \rightarrow 2H^+ + SO_4^{2-}$$

What evidence is there for this? The answer will lie in experiment and so let us return to the bench and find out.

Take two beakers marked A and B and place 25 ml of molar sulphuric acid in each. Add 25 ml of molar sodium hydroxide to each.

The theory suggests that the reaction in each beaker will be:

$$Na^+ + OH^- + H^+ + HSO_4^- \rightarrow Na^+ + HSO_4^- + H_2O$$

bisulphate ion

The bisulphate ion should yield the other hydrogen ion if a further 25 ml of molar sodium hydroxide is added because there will be more hydroxyl ions to draw the hydrogen ions away from the bisulphate.

To verify this, add a further 25 ml of molar sodium hydroxide solution to the solution in beaker B. We should expect the reaction to be:

$$Na^+ + HSO_4^- + Na^+ + OH^- \rightarrow 2Na^+ + SO_4^{2-} + H_2O$$

In beaker A we should now have a solution of sodium ions and bisulphate ions in water. In beaker B there should be a solution of sodium ions and sulphate ions.

If these solutions are evaporated down to a quarter of their original volume and then set aside to crystallise, we should obtain two different crystalline substances. Beaker A should contain crystals of sodium bisulphate and beaker B should contain sodium sulphate crystals.

Do the experiment and find out the answer. Do you obtain two different salts? Is their crystalline shape the same? Do they dissolve equally well in water? What is the effect of the crystals on moist litmus paper? How do they behave on heating?

13.2.

You may not have encountered sodium bisulphate before, but you have certainly met sodium bicarbonate—commonly called baking soda.

How would you go about making it? You will not find a bottle of carbonic acid in the laboratory, but it is possible to make carbonic acid on the spot by bubbling carbon dioxide into water.

$$H_2O + CO_2 \rightarrow H_2CO_3$$

If the carbon dioxide is bubbled into sodium hydroxide solution, the carbonic acid formed will be forced to yield up two hydrogen ions per molecule to combine with the large excess of hydroxyl ions.

$$H_2CO_3 + 2Na^+ + 2OH^- \rightarrow 2Na^+ + CO_3^{2-} + 2H_2O$$

However, if we keep the gas bubbling into the solution for a long time, all the hydroxyl ions will be used up and so some of the hydrogen ions from the excess carbonic acid will join the carbonate ions to give bicarbonate ions.

$$H_2CO_3 + CO_3^{2-} \rightarrow 2HCO_3^-$$

Sodium bicarbonate is not very soluble in water and so if the concentration becomes fairly high, sodium bicarbonate will begin to crystallise out.

Your teacher will provide you with a concentrated solution of sodium hydroxide. Place just enough of the solution in a U-tube to close the bottom of the U. Attach this to a slow source of carbon dioxide. As the gas comes down one limb it will push the solution a little way up the other limb until the gas can bubble through freely but *slowly* (Figure 56).

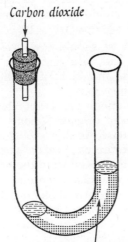

Carbon dioxide

Sodium hydroxide solution

Figure 56

After about fifteen minutes white crystals of sodium bicarbonate will begin to settle out at the bottom of the U-tube.

Summing up so far

It is possible to obtain more than one salt when an acid is allowed to react with an alkali.

The salts in which *some but not all* of the hydrogen ions of the acid have been replaced by metal ions are called **acid salts**. Examples are sodium bisulphate and sodium bicarbonate. The salts in

which *all* of the hydrogen ions of the acid have been replaced by metal ions are called **normal salts**. Examples are sodium sulphate and sodium carbonate. The acid salts are quite definitely salts, but they retain some of the behaviour of an acid because they can still give hydrogen ions away to other substances.

These acid salts are not uncommon. *Sodium bicarbonate* finds many uses besides being a raising agent in baking and we shall investigate some of its properties toward the end of this chapter.

Sodium bisulphate is sold as a cleansing agent for toilets—'cleans and disinfects right round the bend'. In chemistry sets, a powder is included which, when dissolved in water, behaves as an acid. This is often sodium bisulphate.

Sodium bisulphite is used to bleach paper for making newsprint.

Another acid salt which is very common and which is a nuisance is *calcium bicarbonate*, $Ca^{2+}(HCO_3^-)_2$. A great deal of money is spent trying to get rid of it.

It is formed in much the same way as sodium bicarbonate. Rain water is a dilute solution of carbonic acid since the water dissolves carbon dioxide as it falls. A common mineral in this country is calcium carbonate in the form of chalk or limestone. As the rain water containing carbonic acid runs over the rock it slowly dissolves the calcium carbonate to give the soluble acid salt—calcium bicarbonate.

$$\underset{\text{Rain}}{H_2O} + \underset{\text{In the air}}{CO_2} + \underset{\text{Chalk}}{Ca^{2+}CO_3^{2-}} \rightarrow \underset{\text{Calcium bicarbonate.}}{Ca^{2+} + 2HCO_3^-}$$

The calcium bicarbonate solution finds its way into rivers and reservoirs. This water, when it comes as a domestic supply, is very difficult to use for washing. Soap gives a poor lather with it and often a grey scum appears. The water is said to be hard. Next year, when we study the chemistry of soap, we shall discuss this problem more fully.

13.3. Sodium Bicarbonate—maid of all work?

Carry out the following experiments with sodium bicarbonate powder. Record your results carefully and try to work out what is happening at each stage.

(a) Dissolve a little in water and find its pH. An acid salt! Look back to the section on hydrolysis for an explanation (11.2, p. 46).

(b) Heat a little in a dry test-tube and test for

any gases coming off. When no further reaction is taking place, cool the white powder which is left. Add a few drops of any acid. What is the effect? Is any gas given off? Perhaps you understand the name *bi*carbonate now.

(c) Add one inch of dilute hydrochloric acid to a little of the powder in a test-tube. Describe the effect. Which gas is given off?

(d) Repeat (c) using sulphuric acid instead.

(e) Mix some sodium bicarbonate and some citric acid crystals in a *dry* test-tube. Do you recognise the taste of the citric acid? Add a little water and describe the effect.

(f) Repeat the above experiment using tartaric acid.

(g) Mix a little sodium bicarbonate with some tartaric acid and sugar. Taste the dry powder. Do you recognise it?

Sodium bicarbonate hydrolyses in water to give a mildly alkaline solution, which is of use in the treatment of the acid stings of some insects. It is also used in the laboratory to neutralise acid burns on the skin. This solution is a good eye-bath and mouth-wash and the solid makes a satisfactory tooth powder.

When it is heated in an oven it releases carbon dioxide, but twice as much of the gas is released if an acid is mixed with it. And so baking powders are a mixture of sodium bicarbonate and a powdered acid such as tartaric acid or one of its acid salts called cream of tartar.

Many indigestion powders contain sodium bicarbonate to neutralise any excess hydrochloric acid in the stomach.

In some fire extinguishers, a bottle of sulphuric acid is placed near a solution of sodium bicarbonate. When the plunger is struck on the floor, the bottle of acid breaks and the acid reacts with the bicarbonate to generate carbon dioxide. This builds up a pressure which sends a jet of frothy mixture out of the nozzle to extinguish the fire. It is essential that this kind of extinguisher should be rinsed out and refilled as soon as possible after use so that it will be ready for any further emergency.

The mixture in (g) is, of course, sherbet. It is often used to disguise medicines. For example, it disguises the flavour of magnesium sulphate in health salts. Mixed with soluble aspirin it gives the not unpleasant 'Disprin'.

What a versatile substance sodium bicarbonate is!

LOOKING BACK AT CHAPTER 13

Before you leave this chapter, you should *know* and *understand* the meaning of the following:

1. Acid Salt.
2. Normal Salt.
3. Hydrolysis of sodium bicarbonate.

Something to think about

1. What are the formulae of the acid and normal sodium salts of sulphurous acid $((H^+)_2SO_3^{2-})$?

2. Phosphoric acid has a formula $(H^+)_3PO_4^{3-}$. How many salts could be made with sodium hydroxide and this acid? Try to write the formulae for them.

IONS—FREE AND TRAPPED

14

The salts which you have been making in the previous two chapters have all been soluble in water. To recover them as solids you had to allow a solution of the salt to evaporate until crystals were deposited.

We tend to think of substances as being soluble or insoluble in water. However, strictly speaking, *everything* is soluble to some extent. We saw last year that even glass is soluble.

In practice, some salts are so very slightly soluble that we regard them as being insoluble. You have already seen two of these being made—copper silicate and copper ferrocyanide. The bulk of this chapter will be devoted to the study of other 'insoluble' salts.

14.1. A white insoluble salt

Another insoluble salt which you can prepare is barium sulphate. To make it you will require two solutions—one containing a soluble barium salt and the other containing a soluble sulphate. Solutions of barium chloride and sodium sulphate would do. Record the temperatures of the solutions.

Mix the two solutions. What happens?

What evidence is there for a chemical reaction? Allow the solid to settle (Figure 57).

The precipitate is barium sulphate. You will notice that sodium ions and chloride ions are free before and after mixing. The only ions which have reacted are barium ions and sulphate ions. In common with other reactions in which settling takes place, energy is released.

$$Ba^{2+} + SO_4^{2-} \rightarrow Ba^{2+}SO_4^{2-}$$
$$\text{free} \qquad\qquad \text{joined in a solid}$$

The unreacting sodium ions and chloride ions are sometimes called **'spectator ions'**.

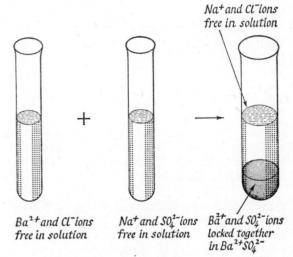

Figure 57

These **'precipitation reactions'**, as they are called, always begin with two soluble compounds in solution so that all the ions are free. On mixing these we are left with a solid containing two species of ions locked together and a solution containing two kinds of ions free.

$$A^+ + B^- + X^+ + Y^- \rightarrow A^+Y^- + X^+ + B^-$$

or, more simply, leaving out the 'spectator ions' from both sides.

$$A^+ + Y^- \rightarrow A^+Y^-$$
$$\text{free} \quad \text{free} \qquad \text{solid containing the}$$
$$\text{A ions} \quad \text{Y ions} \quad \text{ions locked together}$$

14.2. A closer investigation

What do you expect would have happened if you had used barium hydroxide as the source of free barium ions and dilute sulphuric acid as the source of free sulphate ions? Would barium sulphate have been precipitated? Try the experiment and see if this is so. Measure the temperatures before and after this reaction. How does this result compare with that in 14.1?

Filter off any barium sulphate which you obtain.

What might have happened to the hydrogen ions from the dilute sulphuric acid and the hydroxyl ions from the barium hydroxide? Does the temperature change confirm your ideas? Look back to 12.4, p. 51.

Will there be any free ions in the filtrate this time?

Here is an interesting situation. Is it possible that, after mixing the original solutions, *no* free ions are present? You can follow the behaviour of the ions using the conductivity apparatus.

Fill the beaker to about two-thirds of its depth with distilled water and stir in about 5 drops of dilute sulphuric acid. Using the sensitivity control on the panel, get as high a reading on the meter as possible. The hydrogen ions and the sulphate ions in the solution are responsible for its conductivity. Add a spatula full of solid barium hydroxide and gently stir the contents of the beaker. Some of the barium hydroxide will dissolve. Record the meter reading at intervals of about 10 seconds until the reading remains steady for 1 minute or else moves off the scale. Complete the rough graph in your notebooks (Figure 58).

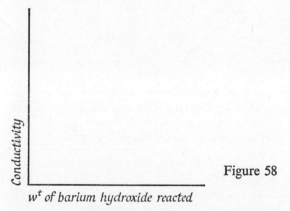

Figure 58

We must try to interpret the graph in terms of our suggested explanation.

During the first part of the graph barium ions and sulphate ions are becoming locked together as insoluble sulphate, $Ba^{2+} + SO_4^{2-} \rightarrow Ba^{2+}SO_4^{2-}$, while hydrogen ions and hydroxyl ions are becoming locked together as water, $H^+ + OH^- \rightarrow H_2O$. The conductivity will therefore drop off to zero because no free ions remain in the solution.

Did your conductivity reading actually reach zero? If not can you suggest any reason for its stopping short?

During the second part of the graph, the solid barium hydroxide in the beaker continues to dissolve and furnish barium ions and hydroxyl ions to the solution. For this reason the conductivity rises.

$$Ba^{2+}(OH^-)_2 \rightarrow Ba^{2+} + 2OH^-$$

Although we cannot see the ions, we have been able to verify our ideas about their behaviour using the conductivity apparatus.

Your teacher may suggest other insoluble salts which you can prepare by this method of precipitation. In each case, try to work out what is happening to the free ions in the two solutions with which you start.

14.3. Soluble or insoluble?

Before deciding which method you are going to use to prepare a salt, you must find out whether it is soluble or insoluble. A soluble salt will be prepared by one of the methods explained in Chapter 12, whereas an insoluble salt will be prepared by precipitation.

Here are some rules which will help you to decide about solubility, at least as far as the more common salts are concerned. It is helpful to know them.

1. Almost all ammonium salts dissolve in water.
2. Almost all nitrates dissolve in water.
3. Almost all salts of the metals in Group I of the Periodic Table dissolve in water.

   With these three statements in mind, it is not too difficult to understand the exceptions to the rest of the rules.
4. Most lead salts do not dissolve in water— (an exception is lead nitrate—see rule 2).
5. Most hydroxides do not dissolve in water— (exceptions are ammonium hydroxide, the hydroxides of Group I metals and also the hydroxides of Group II metals).
6. Most carbonates do not dissolve in water— (exceptions are ammonium carbonate and the carbonates of Group I metals).
7. Most sulphates dissolve in water— (exceptions are lead sulphate and the sulphates of metals in Group II—barium, calcium and strontium).
8. Most chlorides dissolve in water— (exceptions are lead chloride, silver chloride and mercury (I) chloride. Where are these metals found in the Periodic Table?).

14.4. A helpful summary—how to turn one salt into another

The various methods of converting salts into each other can be summarised in a chart as follows. To avoid complications we shall build the table stage by stage.

The method is not necessarily the neatest or most practical way in each case, but it is a helpful guide.

It depends upon the fact that most salts can easily be made into their insoluble carbonates and that the carbonates can easily be made into other salts by using the correct acid.

The carbonates are rather like a roundabout on which several roads converge and from which several roads lead (Figure 59).

The salts we start with must be soluble in water

$$Cu^{2+}CO_3^{2-}+2H^++2NO_3^-\rightarrow$$
$$Cu^{2+}+2NO_3^-+H_2O+CO_2$$

Insoluble carbonates can be converted to oxides by heating them. We therefore have a method of obtaining metal oxides from salts.

(i) Make the carbonate as above.

(ii) Filter it off and heat it.

The oxide is left.

Unfortunately, it is not possible to turn oxides into carbonates and so return to the centre of the diagram. Basic oxides, however, dissolve in acids to give salts and we can join another part of the table and so get to the centre if need be (Figure 60).

One last refinement can be added. If a metal is required from a salt we can sometimes obtain it from the carbonate via the oxide. The oxide can

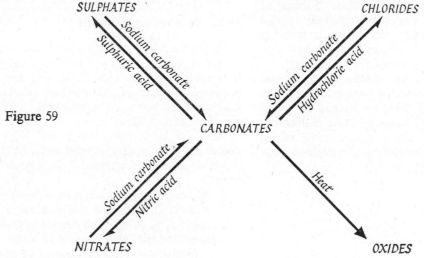

Figure 59

so that their ions can be free. When they are mixed with sodium carbonate solution, the metal ions combine with the carbonate ions and settle as a solid which can be filtered off. We have now reached the 'roundabout'.

To convert a carbonate to a salt we simply dissolve it in the correct acid, evaporate and crystallise the solution.

Let us take an example. We require to convert copper (II) sulphate into copper (II) nitrate.

Take a solution of copper (II) sulphate, add sodium carbonate solution and filter off the copper (II) carbonate.

$$Cu^{2+}+SO_4^{2-}+2Na^++CO_3^{2-}\rightarrow$$
$$Cu^{2+}CO_3^{2-}+2Na^++SO_4^{2-}$$

To make the nitrate, dissolve the filtered copper (II) carbonate in nitric acid, evaporate and crystallise.

be reduced with carbon, hydrogen or carbon monoxide, and so the diagram finally looks like a Union Jack on a flag pole (Figure 61)!

Let us work out some examples in full.

(a) Convert nickel sulphate to nickel oxide.

Dissolve nickel sulphate in water and add sodium carbonate solution. Filter off the green nickel carbonate. Heat it to drive off water until the black nickel oxide is left.

(b) Convert copper powder to copper sulphate.

Heat the powder in an open dish and stir it to give it easy contact with air. Dissolve the black copper (II) oxide in warm dilute sulphuric acid and filter off any unchanged copper. Evaporate the solution to concentrate it. Cover it and set it aside to crystallise.

$$2Cu+O_2\rightarrow2Cu^{2+}O^{2-}$$
$$Cu^{2+}O^{2-}+2H^++SO_4^{2-}\rightarrow Cu^{2+}+SO_4^{2-}+H_2O$$

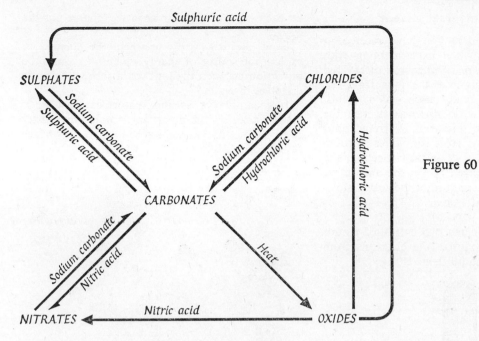

Figure 60

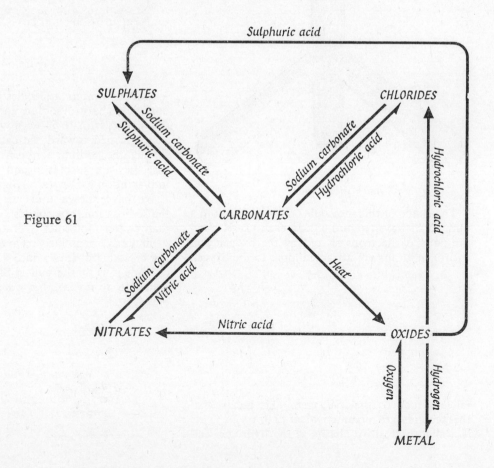

Figure 61

14.5.   Water—the universal solvent

Throughout the course you have received a number of surprises when experimenting with water. One was in 3.4, p. 10 when you discovered that water could easily free the ions from the rigid arrangement in many electrovalent solids. The only other way to do this was to melt the solid. In most cases this took a tremendous amount of heat energy. How can water at room temperature so easily break up the lattice in many electrovalent compounds? To get the answer we must go back to the structure of the water molecule. This was worked out in 4.3, p. 14. Let us revise this here.

An atom of oxygen has two half-filled clouds (Figure 62) and so requires the electrons from two hydrogen atoms to fill them.

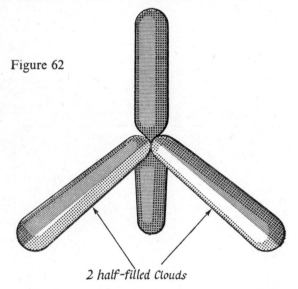

Figure 62

2 half-filled Clouds

The shape of this molecule can be pictured in a number of ways (Figure 63). In each O−H bond the pairs of electrons shared by the oxygen and hydrogen atoms are attracted more to the oxygen

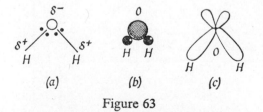

Figure 63

nucleus than to the hydrogen. This means that these bonds are polar covalent (2.3, p. 7). There is a slightly positive charge at the hydrogen end

of each and a slightly negative charge at the oxygen.

How does this structure help the chemist to explain the source of energy which overcomes the attraction between the ions when sodium chloride dissolves in water?

If a sample of sodium chloride, Na^+Cl^-, is placed in water, the polar water molecules cluster round the sodium and chloride ions on the surface of the solid (Figure 64).

● Hydrogen
◉ Oxygen

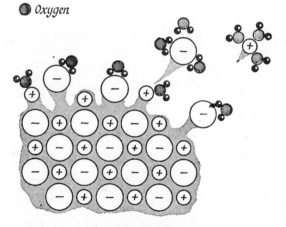

Figure 64

Moving water molecules swarm round the positively charged sodium ions on the surface of the crystal with their negatively charged oxygen atoms turned toward the cations. They then try to pull the sodium ions off the crystal. In this case they are successful and the sodium ions go into solution as $Na^+(aq)$ (Figure 65).

We have shown four water molecules round the sodium ion, but chemists are not certain how many water molecules hydrate each sodium ion.

Similarly, negatively charged chloride ions in the crystal are drawn into solution as hydrated chloride ions by the pull of the positively charged hydrogen atoms in other water molecules (Figure 66).

● Hydrogen
◉ Oxygen

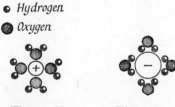

Figure 65   Figure 66

Again it is not certain how many water molecules cluster round one chloride ion so we simply write the hydrated chloride ion as Cl^-(aq).

As sodium ions and chloride ions are being hauled off the lattice into solution, a few of them are attracted back to the crystal lattice and become detached from the swarm of water molecules round them. These ions are redeposited on the crystal surface.

When the solid first dissolves more ions are being pulled off the crystal than are returning to it. If the number of ions leaving the crystal becomes the same as the number being redeposited, the solution is said to be **saturated**. Because of the constant coming and going of ions, the solid lying at the bottom of a saturated solution is always changing.

Polar water molecules will try to do the same to all electrovalent solids. If they are able to detach only a very few ions from a solid, the compound is said to be insoluble.

14.6. When polar meets polar

Your teacher will prepare two solutions for you. One will be of the polar gas hydrogen chloride dissolved in a covalent liquid called toluene. The other will contain the same gas dissolved in water.

Test the two solutions as follows:—
(a) Add litmus to each.
(b) Add magnesium to each.
(c) Add a carbonate to each.
(d) Test the conductivity of each.

Can our theories explain the results?

When hydrogen chloride dissolves in water polar water molecules form up round polar hydrogen chloride molecules as shown in Figure 67.

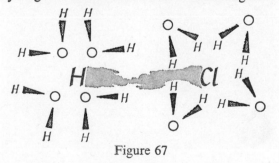

Figure 67

A tug-of-war develops which snaps the $H-Cl$ bond and forms hydrogen ions and chloride ions (10.1, p. 43). The solution therefore contains ions and so conducts electricity. The hydrogen ions are free to affect litmus and free to be replaced by metal ions.

Toluene is almost non-polar. Its molecules are unable to snap the $H-Cl$ bond. The solution, therefore, does not contain ions and so does not conduct electricity. There are no hydrogen ions available to give the other reactions.

You may remember that in 5.2, p. 20 we wrote pure acids as HCl, H_2SO_4, HNO_3, etc. This is to indicate that the pure acids contain few ions. Only when they dissolve in water are large quantities of hydrogen ions liberated along with the corresponding anions.

LOOKING BACK AT CHAPTER 14

Before you leave this chapter, you should **know** and **understand** the meaning of the following:
1. An 'insoluble' salt.
2. Spectator Ions.
3. Precipitation Reactions.
4. Solubility Rules.
5. Converting one salt into another.
6. Polar covalent bonds in water.
7. How water acts as a solvent.
8. A Saturated Solution.

Something to think about

1. From its formula weight water would be expected to be a gas at room temperature. Does its structure help you to understand why this is not so?

2. Calcium sulphate is more soluble in water than barium sulphate is. If the conductivity experiment in 14.2 was repeated with solid calcium hydroxide in place of solid barium hydroxide, what difference would this make to the graph?

3. Here is a rather more difficult question.
The conductivity of limewater is measured and then carbon dioxide gas is bubbled into it for a fairly long time. What shape would the graph be if conductivity was plotted against time?

MAINLY 15 ABOUT SULPHUR

Last year we mentioned that, although not an abundant element in the earth, sulphur is one of the few found uncombined.

Free sulphur occurs in volcanic districts throughout the world—a sign that it may be deposited from hot volcanic gases—but by far the largest amounts are found in Texas.

It has also been mentioned that sulphur is found in the earth combined with metals and we discovered how these metal ores, the sulphides, could be used as a source of metals. Sulphur can also be obtained from them.

There are other compounds containing sulphur in the earth which chemists find useful, for instance, Anhydrite, $Ca^{2+}SO_4^{2-}$ and Barytes or Heavy Spar, $Ba^{2+}SO_4^{2-}$.

Compounds containing sulphur occur in coal and in the gases from oil wells. In natural gas, sulphur compounds are so abundant that France obtains more than enough sulphur from this source to meet her own requirements.

15.1. Extracting sulphur

The Texas deposits occur at a depth of 500 feet, beneath layers of quicksand, clay and limestone. The sulphur is mixed with calcite (calcium carbonate) from which it has to be separated. This presents one difficulty. Another lies in the fact that ordinary mining methods of extraction are unsuitable because of the risk of cave-in and noxious gases.

The method of extracting the sulphur is a most ingenious one called, after its inventor, the Frasch process. Frasch, an American engineer, had observed that the melting point of sulphur is about 13C° above the temperature of boiling water. He considered the idea of melting the sulphur where it lay in the sulphur-calcite mixture, and then raising the molten sulphur to the surface. Frasch had to contend with a certain

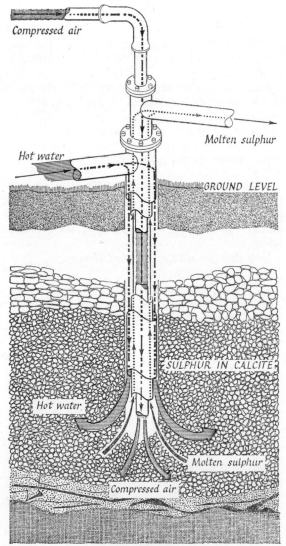

Figure 68

amount of ridicule about his ideas, but the very first trial was successful.

In practice, three concentric pipes are lowered into the deposit (Figure 68).

Superheated water at 160°C (i.e. water heated under pressure) is passed down the outermost pipe. This melts the sulphur. At the same time hot pressurised air is passed down the innermost pipe. The air mixes with the now molten sulphur and a hot froth of steam, water, air and molten sulphur passes up the central pipe. This frothy mixture is run off into immense vats where the sulphur gradually solidifies into blocks, often as big as a large block of flats. It is over 99·5% pure and for most purposes does not require any further purification.

In Frasch's description of the first trial we read that 'within five minutes the receptacles under pressure were opened, and a beautiful stream of the golden fluid shot into the barrels we had ready to receive the product. After pumping for about 15 minutes, the 40 barrels we had supplied were seen to be inadequate. Quickly we threw up embankments and lined them with boards to receive the sulphur that was gushing forth.'

Frasch was overjoyed at the success of the trial. After the sulphur had solidified he admits to mounting the sulphur pile and seating himself on the very top. There he presumably had the last laugh!

15.2. Sulphur in two forms

Chemists know that sulphur can exist in two different crystalline forms or polymorphs as they are called. You may recall investigating other substances which showed the same behaviour. One of the polymorphs of sulphur is stable at room temperature. It is called **rhombic** sulphur because of its crystalline shape (Figure 69).

You can make crystals of rhombic sulphur quite easily using powdered sulphur. Shake some of it with carbon disulphide until no more dissolves. Filter the solution and allow the filtrate to evaporate slowly in a fume cupboard. Take care, because carbon disulphide vapour is *very* inflammable. You will get yellow transparent crystals of rhombic sulphur.

There is evidence that the sulphur atoms in rhombic sulphur are arranged in rings of eight (Figure 70).

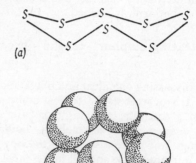

Figure 70

These S_8 rings are packed together in such a way as to give crystals of rhombic sulphur.

The second polymorph of sulphur is rather unusual. It exists only between 96° and 119°C and is called **monoclinic** sulphur. Crystals of monoclinic sulphur are also built up of S_8 molecules, but this polymorph has a lower density. This suggests that there is a looser packing of the rings. Crystals of monoclinic sulphur are shown in Figure 71.

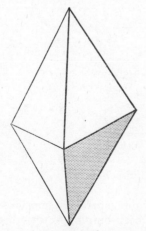

A crystal of rhombic sulphur

Figure 69

Crystals of monoclinic sulphur

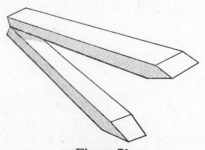

Figure 71

You can obtain well-formed crystals of mono-clinic sulphur by making a saturated solution of powdered sulphur in boiling toluene (B.P. 110°C). The clear solution should be allowed to cool slowly in a beaker of boiling water to keep the temperature above 96°C.

If these crystals are cooled by leaving them in the air, in about 24 hours they become opaque. Do you find that they crumble into a powder very easily?

The powder is made up of small crystals of rhombic sulphur. As the sulphur cools below 96°C energy is lost. This results in the rings packing more tightly together and the more dense rhombic polymorph is formed.

15.3. Heating sulphur—careful observation pays

When discussing chemical and physical changes in Form I, you were asked to heat some sulphur slowly in a test-tube and to look carefully for physical changes such as melting, boiling and condensing. You were also asked to copy Figure 72 into your notebook and fill in the labels.

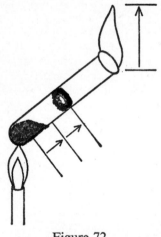

Figure 72

Do this experiment again using about two inches of powdered sulphur in the test-tube. Watch what happens to the element at the bottom of the test-tube as well as at the mouth. Heat the sulphur until it boils (445°C), recording in your notebook any changes which you see in its viscosity (thickness) and colour.

Quickly pour the final dark liquid into some cold water in a beaker. Pick out the solid which is formed. How would you describe it? Have you discovered that it behaves rather like elastic?

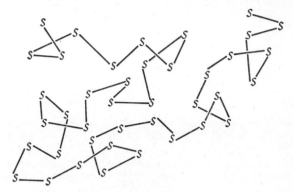

Figure 73

This kind of sulphur is called **plastic** sulphur. Chemists believe that the loose ends of broken S_8 rings couple up with one another to form very long tangled chains of sulphur atoms. These tangled chains can be stretched, giving plastic sulphur rubbery properties (Figure 73).

Sulphur vapour, some of which sublimes on the test-tube, is made up of S_2 molecules, each S_8 ring having been split into 4 pairs of S_2 molecules. It is believed that some monatomic molecules of sulphur are obtained when sulphur vapour is heated to 2000°C (Figure 74).

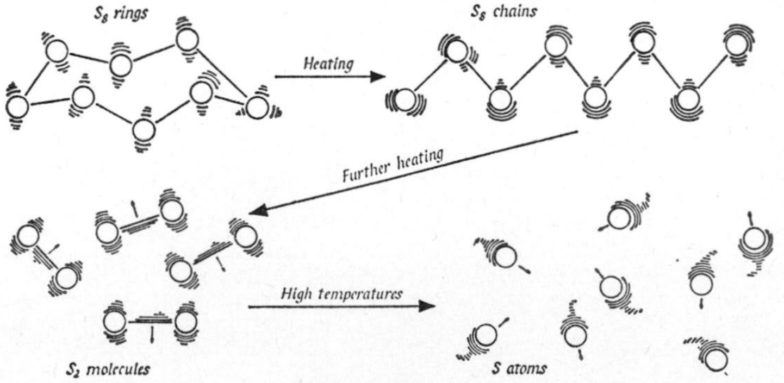

S_8 rings → Heating → S_8 chains → Further heating → S_2 molecules → High temperatures → S atoms

Figure 74

During your experiment most of the sulphur vapour has been burning to form the gas sulphur dioxide which, as you know, has a most un-pleasant smell. However, it is a most useful and important gas—as you will discover in Chapter 16.

15.4. Sulphur dioxide from sulphur compounds

Last year you roasted at least one metal sulphide in the air on a piece of asbestos tape. You could repeat the experiment now using as many sulphides as you can get. In how many cases can you smell sulphur dioxide gas?

When sulphides are roasted in the air like this on a large scale—with a view to recovering the metal—it is often necessary to collect the sulphur dioxide formed because it is poisonous. Then, either sulphur is obtained from it or it is used to prepare other compounds. You will see how this can be done in the next chapter.

We mentioned that sulphates are other naturally occurring compounds which contain sulphur. Perhaps roasting these in the air will give sulphur dioxide too. Put some powdered calcium, barium or magnesium sulphate on a piece of asbestos tape and roast it strongly in the air. Can you detect sulphur dioxide? If not, it may be that the amounts of sulphur dioxide formed are so small that we need a more sensitive method of detecting it.

You will see in the next chapter that, in many of its reactions, sulphur dioxide tries to combine with oxygen to form sulphur trioxide, SO_3. It cannot combine very well with atmospheric oxygen, but it can combine with the oxygen contained in compounds called iodates, for example, sodium iodate, $Na^+IO_3^-$. When the oxygen is removed from iodate ions, iodine is left. This gives a deep blue colour in the presence of starch.

A convenient and delicate way of testing for sulphur dioxide is to use a filter paper which has been soaked in a solution containing iodate ions and starch. When this gas comes into contact with paper, a blue colour (starch+iodine) is seen.

Try the test by burning a little sulphur on asbestos tape. Hold a piece of starch/iodate paper above it. Can you see a blue colour appearing on the paper?

Now try heating the sulphates again using this more sensitive way of testing for sulphur dioxide. Have you had any success?

15.5. A responsive sulphate

By now you will have discovered that most sulphates do not give sulphur dioxide when heated

in the air. This is unfortunate because it means that a country like Britain, although it has plenty of naturally occurring sulphates, has still to import quantities of sulphur with which to make sulphur dioxide. However, chemists have been successful in obtaining sulphur dioxide using the deposits of anhydrite, a form of calcium sulphate, found in the North of England.

You can try this experiment shown in Figure 75. Use a finely powdered mixture of equal bulks of carbon, silica and calcium sulphate. You will have to heat the mixture strongly for about five minutes.

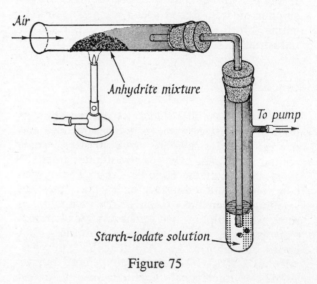

Figure 75

Do you agree that sulphur dioxide has been formed?

Last year you saw that hydrochloric, sulphuric and nitric acids can push other acids from their salts. Here you have another example of the same kind of reaction. The silica, an acidic oxide, pushes sulphur dioxide from a sulphate. This is because the sulphur dioxide escapes as a gas, while silica remains as a solid which does not evaporate. It may be that the high temperature reached by the hot carbon helps the reaction to take place.

When the United States decided to ration sulphur some years ago, chemists in Britain were forced to use anhydrite to supplement our sulphur supply. How convenient it was when they found that their factory was built on anhydrite. There was literally a mine on the doorstep!

THE OXIDES OF SULPHUR

In the previous chapter we repeatedly met the gas sulphur dioxide. Let us spend some time investigating it further because it is a very important gas industrially.

16.1.

(a) One of the first things we noticed about it early in the first year was its unpleasant smell and dry taste. Bad smells are characteristic of gases containing sulphur. Oxygen and sulphur are in the same column of the Periodic Table. The oxygen compounds are odourless or at least pleasant smelling. When the oxygen in the compound is replaced by sulphur, bad smells become common. For example, water (H_2O) is odourless, but hydrogen sulphide (H_2S) smells of bad eggs. Alcohol (C_2H_5OH) has a fruity smell, but its neighbour thioalcohol (C_2H_5SH) has an almost unbearable smell.

(b) The gas is normally stored in the laboratory in glass or metal cylinders. It is not just a compressed gas in the cylinder, but a liquefied gas. Sulphur dioxide is fairly easy to liquefy either by cooling or compression. We have met the idea that cooling slows down molecular movement and causes the molecules to gather together as droplets of liquid. Compression does not slow the molecules, but it brings them closer together thus giving them a better opportunity of sticking together in clusters to form droplets.

A simple laboratory experiment shows sulphur dioxide being liquefied by cooling (Figure 76).

Sulphur dioxide can be released from a sulphite in the same way as carbon dioxide from a carbonate. Place some crystals of sodium sulphite in the bottom of a bottle and add moderately concentrated hydrochloric acid.

$$(Na^+)_2SO_3^{2-} + 2H^+ + 2Cl^- \rightarrow$$
$$2Na^+ + 2Cl^- + H_2O + SO_2(g)$$

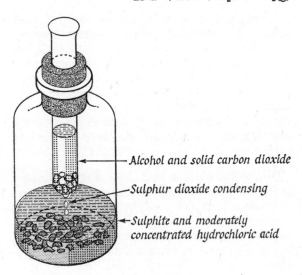

Alcohol and solid carbon dioxide

Sulphur dioxide condensing

Sulphite and moderately concentrated hydrochloric acid

Figure 76

The test-tube in the stopper contains a freezing mixture of solid carbon dioxide in alcohol. As the sulphur dioxide meets the cold surface of the tube (about $-70°C$) it condenses and drops off as a pale yellow liquid. The **boiling point** of liquid sulphur dioxide is $-10°C$ at atmospheric pressure.

(c) Fill a dry test-tube with sulphur dioxide gas from the cylinder. Close the tube with your finger and invert it in a beaker of water. Open the tube under water. What happens? Test the solution with litmus paper. The sulphur dioxide must have reacted with water to release hydrogen ions.

$$H_2O + SO_2 \rightarrow 2H^+ + SO_3^{2-}$$
$$\text{sulphurous acid}$$
$$\text{or} \rightarrow H^+ + HSO_3^-$$

This is the reaction of an acidic oxide which we met in Form I.

66

You may have time to test the conductivity of the solution to see if the acid formed is strong or weak (3.5, p. 12).

Sulphurous acid forms two different sodium salts corresponding to the two sodium salts of sulphuric acid. Sodium bisulphite has the formula $Na^+HSO_3^-$ and sodium sulphite $(Na^+)_2SO_3^{2-}$. An acid like this is said to be **dibasic** (or **diprotic**—providing two protons or hydrogen ions).

16.2. The effect of an electron donor on sulphur dioxide

We did a similar experiment with carbon dioxide. A good electron donor (reducing agent) is a metal like magnesium. Burn a strip of magnesium in a jar of sulphur dioxide. Is there any evidence for the reduction of the sulphur dioxide? Is there any magnesium oxide or sulphur visible? Would this equation represent the facts?

$$2Mg+SO_2 \rightarrow 2Mg^{2+}O^{2-}+S$$

16.3. The effect of an electron acceptor on sulphur dioxide or sulphurous acid

Sulphur has more than one valency number. In the case of sulphur dioxide (which gives sulphurous acid in solution) its valency number is 4. In sulphur trioxide the valency number is 6. There is a tendency for elements of variable valency number to change from one valency number to another given the right conditions.

If an electron donor in the experiment above has produced sulphur from sulphur dioxide, an electron acceptor might be expected to give SO_3 from SO_2, or SO_4^{2-} from SO_3^{2-}.

The sulphate ion is colourless (3.1, p. 9) and so we shall require some way of identifying it. In 14.1, p. 56 we found a very insoluble sulphate—barium sulphate. If a solution containing barium ions is mixed with a solution containing sulphate ions a very insoluble white precipitate forms. This precipitate will not dissolve even in dilute hydrochloric acid.

$$Ba^{2+}+SO_4^{2-} \rightarrow \underset{\substack{\text{white and insoluble} \\ \text{in dilute acid.}}}{Ba^{2+}SO_4^{2-}}$$

Try mixing a solution of barium chloride with a solution of any sulphate. Have we now a test for the sulphate ion? This would have to be checked by applying the same test to the sulphite ion.

Add barium chloride to a solution of sodium sulphite. Is there a white precipitate? Is it more soluble in dilute hydrochloric acid than barium sulphate is?

Would we, on the basis of these tests, be able to distinguish between the sulphate ion and the sulphite ion?

What efficient electron acceptors do you think we should try in our attempt to oxidise (de-electronise) the sulphur dioxide or the sulphite ion? Can you think of any elements which would be suitable? Where in the Periodic Table are the elements with almost complete shells?

For convenience we shall use a solution of a sulphite, for example, sulphurous acid or sodium sulphite, for these experiments.

(i) Halogens

Mix the sulphite solution with a solution of chlorine, bromine or iodine.

What evidence do you see for the fact that these halogens have become halide ions? Consult the chemical cupboard to check on the colour of halide ions. Test the solution that is left with barium chloride solution and hydrochloric acid to see if any sulphate ion is detectable.

(ii) Cations of metals far down the reactivity series

Ions such as Ag^+ seemed fairly ready to accept electrons from metals further up the reactivity series (7.6, p. 28). Let us see if silver ions will accept electrons from sulphite ions.

Warm in a beaker of hot water, the sulphite solution with silver nitrate solution to which a few drops of ammonia have been added. Is there any evidence for the formation of silver? Remember that silver does not always appear as a shiny metal but often as a grey powder. Test the solution as before for sulphate ions. What is the result?

(iii) Other cations

Metals such as iron produce ions of more than one valency number (Fe^{3+} and Fe^{2+}). It is unlikely that a metal so far up the reactivity series will be reduced from its ions. However, it may be possible to persuade the iron (III) ions to accept one electron and become iron (II) ions.

Use a solution of iron (III) chloride to which a little dilute hydrochloric acid has been added. Test the final mixture for sulphate ions.

16.4.

We have spoken quite glibly about electron donors and acceptors, but we have little experimental evidence for these statements. We must try to detect any electron flow from the sulphite solution to the other solutions mentioned above.

Place a plug of glass wool at the bend of a U-tube (Figure 77). Prepare the sulphite solution in

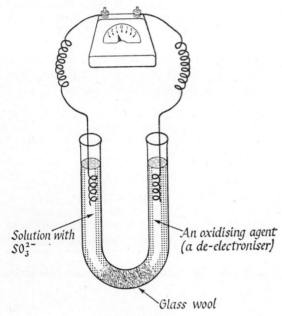

Solution with SO_3^{2-}

An oxidising agent (a de-electroniser)

Glass wool

Figure 77

one test-tube and the other solution in another test-tube. *At the same time* pour the two solutions into the U-tube so that the levels in the limbs of the U-tube remain equal. Place an electrode (carbon or platinum) in each limb of the tube and connect them to a voltmeter or a microammeter. If you obtain a positive meter reading then the electrode attached to the negative terminal of the meter will be dipping in the electron donor and the other electrode will be in the electron acceptor.

Is the sulphite solution the electron donor in each case?

If we try to represent these reactions by means of equations, we should take into consideration this electrical aspect of them. There are certain conventions used in writing these and we shall explain them below.

This particular kind of equation is known as an **ion-electron equation.**

In each of the above experiments we began with sulphite ions and ended with sulphate ions.

Since the reactions took place in the presence of water we take this into account. To make this transformation we require more oxygen which we assume comes from the water.

$$SO_3^{2-} + H_2O \rightarrow SO_4^{2-} + 2H^+$$

This will leave us with two hydrogen ions on the right-hand side. To complete the equation we add up the electric charges on each side.

$$\underbrace{SO_3^{2-} + H_2O}_{charge = -2} \rightarrow \underbrace{SO_4^{2-} + 2H^+}_{charge = 0}$$

The equation is balanced electrically by adding two electrons to the right-hand side giving—

$$SO_3^{2-} + H_2O \rightarrow SO_4^{2-} + 2H^+ + 2e$$

This reaction is one which *gives out electrons*. This equation is an attempt to express the experimental facts. Equations for the electron acceptors are even easier.

(i) *Halogens*

$$\left. \begin{array}{l} \underset{\text{green}}{Cl_2} + 2e \rightarrow 2Cl^- \\ \underset{\text{brown}}{Br_2} + 2e \rightarrow 2Br^- \\ \underset{\text{brown}}{I_2} + 2e \rightarrow 2I^- \end{array} \right\} \text{colourless}$$

(ii) *Silver ion*

$$\underset{\text{colourless}}{Ag^+} + e \rightarrow \underset{\text{grey}}{Ag}$$

(iii) *Iron (III) ion*

$$Fe^{3+} + e \rightarrow Fe^{2+}$$

It seems from these experiments that sulphur dioxide, or the sulphite ion in solution, is very readily oxidised (de-electronised) to the sulphate ion—an increase in the valency number of sulphur from four to six.

Another way of looking at the same facts is to say that sulphite ion is a good electron donor.

16.5.

Girls will appreciate that the washing of white woollen garments eventually results in the white becoming yellow or grey. By the end of a season white cricket sweaters have lost much of their appearance. Any attempt to bleach woollens with bleaches of the common household type usually ends in disaster. The wool tends to disintegrate in this type of bleach.

Woollens can be safely bleached, however, with a sulphite. The beautiful white knitwear we associate with the Shetland Islands (Fair Isle) is still bleached by an apparently primitive method. The garment is soaked in water and then stretched on a wooden frame in a shed. A lump of sulphur is lit in the shed and the door is closed. After a few hours the garment is removed from the atmosphere of sulphur dioxide. It is not only white but also soft and pleasant to the touch.

The sulphur dioxide has dissolved in the water in the wet fabric to give sulphurous acid which has done the bleaching.

As mentioned in 13.2, p. 54 sulphites and bisulphites are used to bleach paper pulp. The natural colour of the pulp is yellow but this is bleached white. When paper is exposed to air and sunlight for a while the natural yellow colour returns. You have probably seen this effect on old newspapers and books.

Let us sum up the properties of sulphur dioxide.
(i) It is a gas with an unpleasant smell and taste.
(ii) It is easily liquefied.
(iii) It is very soluble in water giving sulphurous acid, which is dibasic (diprotic).
(iv) It is a good electron donor.
(v) It is a safe bleach for wool and paper.

In each of the reactions in 16.3 we succeeded in converting SO_3^{2-} into SO_4^{2-}. Since sulphuric acid is much more important than sulphurous acid it would be very useful to be able to convert one into the other. Unfortunately, the methods used in 16.3 bring with them some complications. In each case the sulphuric acid is mixed with other products such as chlorides, bromides, iodides and iron (II) salts.

How much more convenient it would be if we could convert sulphur dioxide directly into sulphur trioxide and then dissolve the product in water to give sulphuric acid. In the next chapter we shall investigate this possibility.

LOOKING BACK AT CHAPTER 16

Before you leave this chapter, you should *know* and *understand* the meaning of the following:
1. Dibasic (Diprotic) Acid.
2. SO_3^{2-} as an electron donor.
3. Tests for sulphate and sulphite ions.
4. Ion-electron Equations.

17
SULPHURIC ACID—THE LIFE BLOOD OF INDUSTRY

Later in this chapter we shall discover something of the vital importance of sulphuric acid. Millions of tons of it are made every year to supply a variety of industries. How is this accomplished?

17.1.

At the end of the last chapter we remarked that it would be very convenient if sulphur dioxide and oxygen would combine directly to give sulphur trioxide.

Let us visualise the problem (Figure 78).

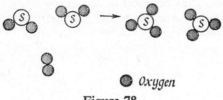

🔴 *Oxygen*

Figure 78

Imagine that these gas molecules are moving about quite vigorously colliding with, and bouncing off, each other. The reaction of the sulphur dioxide molecules with oxygen molecules must depend upon a collision between them which will be sufficiently violent to smash the molecules. The bits may then be regrouped to give sulphur trioxide molecules.

At room temperature the chance of a collision as violent as this is evidently almost impossible. Sulphur dioxide and oxygen can be mixed and left at room temperature for a very long time before even a trace of sulphur trioxide can be detected.

The obvious thing to do is to increase the temperature and make the molecules move faster so that the collisions will be more effective in producing sulphur trioxide.

Set up an apparatus as shown in Figure 79. Allow the sulphur dioxide and oxygen mixture to flow through the hot tube. Are any white steamy fumes of sulphur trioxide to be seen?

Unfortunately, if sulphur trioxide molecules are heated too much they break down to give sulphur dioxide and oxygen; and so the very

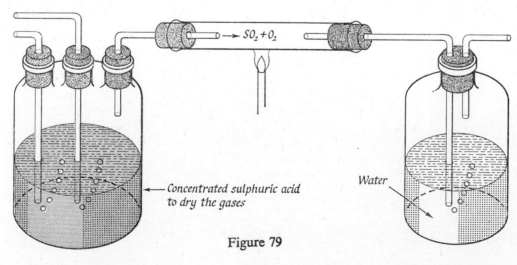

← Concentrated sulphuric acid to dry the gases

Water

Figure 79

process which is making the sulphur trioxide more quickly is also breaking it more quickly. The reaction goes forward and backward at the same time. This is known as a **reversible reaction** and is shown by the double arrows below.

$$2SO_2 + O_2 \rightleftharpoons 2SO_3$$

There comes a point at which SO_3 molecules are being broken as quickly as they are being made. This situation is said to be a **chemical equilibrium**. It is something like trying to run up a descending escalator which is going as quickly as you are. You are getting nowhere fast! In fact, for all your efforts, you are remaining still.

If only you could somehow slow down the escalator and yet maintain your own effort! Only if this happened could you hope to reach the top.

In the reaction, the 'descending escalator' is the breaking up of the SO_3. The 'climbing effort' is the combination of SO_2 and O_2. The only way to slow down the 'escalator' is to reduce the temperature, but that will automatically slow down the 'climber'.

17.2.

It so happens that a method has been discovered which allows the SO_2 and O_2 molecules to meet and collide successfully while keeping the temperature down to about 450°C. This is done by providing the reacting gases with a large surface to which they are attracted and on which they can meet in such a way as to produce the sulphur trioxide. This surface is usually a fine deposit of platinum on the strands of asbestos wool. A very small amount of platinum can be spread out to cover an area of several acres! The platinum is not used up in the reaction for the same piece of platinised asbestos can be used over and over again to produce sulphur trioxide.

A substance which speeds up a chemical reaction but is not used up itself is called a **catalyst**. Let us see this catalyst at work. Insert it in the combustion tube of the apparatus in the previous experiment (Figure 79). Heat it gently and watch for the smoky wisps of sulphur trioxide gas emerging from the catalyst. Has our problem been solved?

This particular process is so important that it has been given a special name—**the contact process**.

In industry another catalyst has been discovered which is cheaper and more efficient than platinised asbestos. It is vanadium pentoxide in the form of pellets. Your teacher may have some and use them in place of the platinised asbestos.

How catalysts work is not yet fully understood, but two facts emerge—(a) the area of the surface of the catalyst is important and (b) a catalyst for one reaction is not necessarily a catalyst for another. Sometimes catalysts seem to fit *one* reaction in the way that a special key fits *one* lock. We shall meet this fact again next year when we come to study the behaviour of some of the catalysts in nature called enzymes.

17.3.

We have now succeeded in getting from sulphur to sulphur trioxide.

$$\text{Sulphur} \xrightarrow{\text{air}} \text{sulphur dioxide} \xrightarrow[\text{+catalyst}]{\text{air}} \text{sulphur trioxide.}$$

All we have to do is to dissolve the sulphur trioxide in water to obtain sulphuric acid.

If you have been doing this in the experiment in 17.2 you will have noticed that the gas is not dissolving very efficiently in water. Clouds of it are passing through the water and escaping. The gas is too precious for this to be allowed. The story goes that in the first contact plant built, the chemists tried to absorb the gas in water. So much gas escaped and filled the factory that the plant had to be shut down temporarily. This last problem has been very neatly solved.

It has been found that very concentrated sulphuric acid containing about 2% of water is an excellent absorber of sulphur trioxide. As the sulphur trioxide is absorbed, measured quantities of water are added to keep the concentration of the acid roughly constant. In this way the volume of the acid steadily increases and the excess can be drawn off leaving enough acid to continue absorbing the sulphur trioxide.

If the sulphur trioxide is absorbed in the sulphuric acid without the addition of water we obtain a 'super concentrated' sulphuric acid called fuming sulphuric acid or oleum. You will meet this substance again when we come to study the manufacture of detergents next year.

17.4. The acid with the high boiling point

Concentrated sulphuric acid is an oily liquid with a specific gravity of about 1·8. Its boiling point is in the region of 340°C. This last property is of value in the preparation of other acids.

If we mix any nitrate with concentrated sulphuric acid we get something like this.

$$H_2SO_4 + Na^+NO_3^- \rightarrow Na^+HSO_4^- + HNO_3(g)$$

This is a mixture of four substances. When the temperature is raised, the substance with the lowest boiling point will distil off first. In this case the hydrogen nitrate gas distils off and can be condensed as concentrated nitric acid.

Similarly, concentrated sulphuric acid reacts with a chloride.

$$H_2SO_4 + K^+Cl^- \rightarrow K^+HSO_4^- + HCl(g)$$

The hydrogen chloride gas distils off at room temperature, reacts with the moisture in the air and gives steamy droplets of hydrochloric acid.

Perhaps more important than these two is the displacement of phosphoric acid from phosphate rock (mainly calcium phosphate).

$$3H_2SO_4 + (Ca^{2+})_3(PO_4^{3-})_2 \rightarrow 3Ca^{2+}SO_4^{2-} + 2H_3PO_4$$

The phosphoric acid is used in the manufacture of fertilisers such as ammonium hydrogen phosphate (20.3, p. 87).

Thus the high boiling point of concentrated sulphuric acid enables it to displace other acids of lower boiling point.

It is worth carrying out these three reactions with very small quantities of the salts and the acid. No more than half-an-inch of the acid should be taken in a test-tube. Your teacher may prefer to demonstrate these to you if he considers them too dangerous. *On no account should they be carried out on your own without supervision.*

The first reaction applies to *any* nitrate. If we are examining a substance and find that it gives off nitric acid when it is treated with concentrated sulphuric acid, then that substance must be a nitrate. The nitric acid is identified by allowing it to come in contact with a piece of copper. This produces brown fumes (19.5, p. 81). This is a useful test for a nitrate. Similarly, we now have tests for a chloride and a phosphate provided we can identify the acid gases displaced.

17.5. The acid with an attraction for water

Half-fill a test-tube with water and cautiously add concentrated sulphuric acid from a dropper. Stir the solution after each drop has been added. What do you notice about the temperature of the water? Do not add any more than five drops of

acid. This effect is mainly due to the hydration of the protons released by the acid.

$$H_2SO_4 + H_2O \rightarrow H^+(aq) + HSO_4^-(aq)$$

The combination of the hydrogen ions with water is very exothermic.

On no account should water be added to the concentrated acid, because sufficient heat will be generated in the drop of water to convert it instantly into steam. The sudden expansion of the drop will cause the acid to spit and corrosive droplets will be scattered around.

This great attraction for water can be shown in many ways.

(i) Half-fill two small beakers—one with concentrated sulphuric acid and one with water. Place them side by side and cover them with a large beaker or bell jar. Set them aside for a few days (Figure 80). What do you notice?

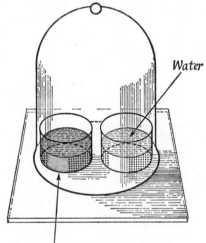

Water

Concentrated sulphuric acid

Figure 80

(ii) Crystals often contain water as part of their structure. The colour of the crystals is sometimes affected by the presence of water. One well-known example is copper sulphate which, as blue crystals, has the formula $Cu^{2+}SO_4^{2-}.5H_2O$.

Cover a blue copper sulphate crystal with concentrated sulphuric acid and set it aside for a while. What happens to its colour? Is there any rise in temperature to indicate a reaction? Pour off the acid and carefully cover the crystal with water. What happens to the colour now?

Account for these colour changes. What colour is the dehydrated copper (II) ion?

(iii) If there are no water molecules in a crystal

and if the compound contains hydrogen and oxygen, the sulphuric acid will collect the hydrogen and oxygen from different parts of the molecule to make water. The water will then hydrate the hydrogen ions of the acid.

This effect can be seen with carbohydrates. The name indicates the elements present.

Make a small quantity of a syrupy solution of cane sugar in warm water in a large beaker. Cool the solution before adding concentrated sulphuric acid, a little at a time. Do you recognise the smell of the mixture? Eventually enough spongy carbon should be left to hold a glass rod upright in it. This form of carbon is known as sugar charcoal.

$$C_{12}H_{22}O_{11} \rightarrow 12C + 11H_2O$$
cane sugar $\qquad$ (combined with the acid)

Other carbohydrates are paper and wood. A black residue of carbon is also formed when these substances are dipped into concentrated sulphuric acid.

Concentrated sulphuric acid is a very dangerous substance and, in most industrial laboratories, protective clothing and goggles are worn while it is being used. Therefore, do not be disappointed if your teacher, in the interests of your safety, does all the experiments involving concentrated sulphuric acid as demonstrations.

17.6. The acid which accepts electrons

Set up the conductivity apparatus. Place one inch of concentrated sulphuric acid in the beaker and measure its conductivity. (Concentrated sulphuric acid is about 18 M.) Compare this reading with that obtained for an inch of molar sulphuric acid.

We might expect that the more concentrated acid would contain many more ions per litre and would therefore be the better conductor of the two (5.5, p. 21). In practice this is not so.

The conclusion must be that, although the concentrated acid contains about eighteen times as much acid as the dilute solution, it does not contain eighteen times as many ions. A large number of the hydrogen and bisulphate ions must be combined as hydrogen sulphate molecules.

$$H^+ + HSO_4^- \rightleftharpoons H_2SO_4$$

The bolder arrow shows that most of the sulphuric acid is present as H_2SO_4 and only a small amount of it is broken up into free hydrogen and bisulphate ions. As the acid is diluted, more and more of the H_2SO_4 molecules break up

(dissociate) to give free hydrogen ions, bisulphate ions and some sulphate ions.

Another piece of evidence to support this is given by this experiment. Take a strip of blue litmus paper and moisten one half of it. Dry off the excess water with filter paper. Drop the strip on to the surface of some concentrated sulphuric acid. What happens to the wet half of the strip compared with the dry half? Make your observation quickly before the paper is dehydrated by the acid (17.5 (iii)).

To some extent these results will help us to understand the following reactions.

(i) Sulphuric acid and metals

In Chapter 7.3, p. 26 we found that only a few metals react with *dilute* acid. The metals are those which are above hydrogen in the reactivity series and are capable of transferring electrons from themselves to the hydrogen ions, for instance, zinc.

$$Zn \rightarrow Zn^{2+} + 2e$$
$$2H^+ + 2e \rightarrow H_2$$

In these cases, it is the hydrogen ions which are the electron acceptors and there is an abundance of them.

Let us find out the action of *concentrated* sulphuric acid on metals.

Cover a small piece of copper with concentrated sulphuric acid and warm it. Is there any reaction? Is any gas given off which you can identify? It is not the hydrogen ions which are affected this time, but possibly the H_2SO_4 molecules or bisulphate ions. Cool the solution and add it carefully to an inch of water in a beaker. Filter it. Is there any evidence for the formation of Cu^{2+}?

The acid has accepted electrons from the copper to allow copper (II) ions to form.

$$Cu + 2H_2SO_4 \rightarrow Cu^{2+} + SO_4^{2-} + SO_2(g) + 2H_2O$$

It is not clearly understood how the sulphuric acid molecules or bisulphate ions take up these electrons, but they do so if the acid is warm and concentrated. The metals do not have to be in the mazit group for this kind of reaction to take place.

(ii) Sulphuric acid and non-metals

Dilute sulphuric acid has no reaction with non-metals. They are usually electron acceptors and so have no tendency to contribute electrons to a hydrogen ion.

However, with hot concentrated acid, a reaction does occur.

Warm a small piece of carbon (charcoal) with concentrated sulphuric acid.

Can you identify the two gases given off?

Try to write an equation to sum up the reaction.

LOOKING BACK AT CHAPTER 17

Before you leave this chapter, you should *know* and *understand* the meaning of the following:

1. Reversible Reaction
2. Chemical Equilibrium.
3. A Catalyst.
4. Dehydration.

Figure 81.—*It has been said that if you know how much sulphuric acid a nation uses you have some idea of that country's prosperity. The chart shows some of the variety of uses to which it is put.*

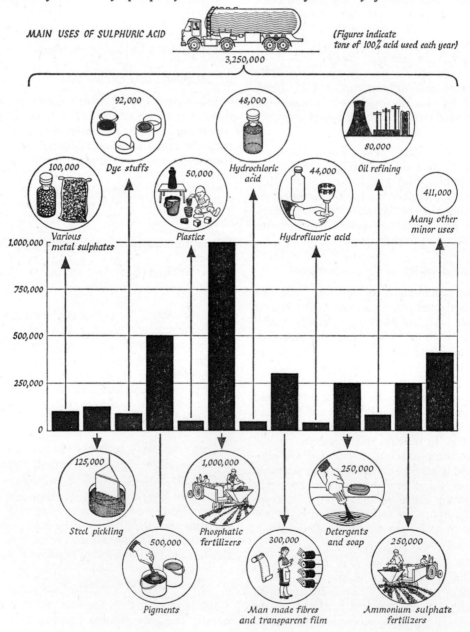

MAIN USES OF SULPHURIC ACID

(Figures indicate tons of 100% acid used each year)

3,250,000

92,000 Dye stuffs

48,000 Hydrochloric acid

80,000 Oil refining

100,000 Various metal sulphates

50,000 Plastics

44,000 Hydrofluoric acid

411,000 Many other minor uses

1,000,000
750,000
500,000
250,000
0

125,000 Steel pickling

500,000 Pigments

1,000,000 Phosphatic fertilizers

300,000 Man made fibres and transparent film

250,000 Detergents and soap

250,000 Ammonium sulphate fertilizers

18 INACTIVE BUT NOT INERT

When you were investigating the composition of the air in Form I, you discovered that four-fifths of it by volume consisted of an unreactive gas which was called nitrogen. It did not combine with either hot copper or smouldering phosphorus. Since then you have come across ammonium salts, nitric acid and nitrates, all compounds which contain combined nitrogen. It would seem that although nitrogen is inactive it is by no means totally idle or inert. It can be made to combine with elements but a great deal of energy is required to make nitrogen compounds. In this chapter we shall discover how some of these compounds are made.

18.1. Nitrogen and oxygen

You saw in Chapter 17 the route by which sulphuric acid is formed.

$$S \rightarrow SO_2 \rightarrow SO_3 \xrightarrow{H_2O} H_2SO_4$$

It seems reasonable to suppose that this might also be a route to the formation of nitric acid.

$$N_2 \rightarrow \text{oxides of nitrogen} \xrightarrow{H_2O} HNO_3$$

The problem is how to make the nitrogen combine with oxygen. Simply heating a mixture of nitrogen and oxygen does not help at all—this just gives us hot air! More energy is needed than can be obtained in this way. The following demonstration experiment shows the source of this energy.

The flask in Figure 82 contains a mixture of nitrogen and oxygen—air will do.
Using an induction coil you can pass a series of electric sparks between the two platinum wires for several minutes. Do you see any colour appearing in the flask?

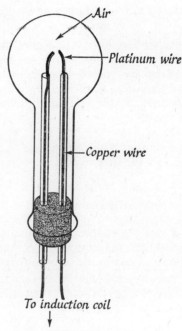

Figure 82

After switching off the current smell the gases in the flask. Is it just air in the flask now? Pour about 2 ml of water into the flask and shake it with the contents. Test the solution with litmus. What happens? Can you interpret the experiment? Remember that oxides of non-metals which dissolve in water form acids.

This experiment shows that nitrogen can be made to combine with oxygen if sufficient energy is supplied. The same reaction takes place in the atmosphere during lightning storms. This is one way of forming nitric acid, but there is the problem of energy supply because of the high cost of electricity. A better method will be discussed in the next chapter.

18.2. Nitrogen and hydrogen

Another common compound of nitrogen is ammonia gas, NH_3. Do you think you could recognise this gas by its smell? It is the gas you can detect if you *cautiously* sniff the ammonium hydroxide bottle. Try it!

Now we have the problem of trying to get nitrogen and hydrogen to combine. Once again heating does not help. What is to be the source of energy this time?

Since sparking a mixture of nitrogen and oxygen caused combination, the same experiment could be tried using a mixture of nitrogen and hydrogen.

Your teacher may have cylinders of these gases available. Using the apparatus in Figure 82, electric sparks are passed through the mixture for several minutes. Can you see any obvious change occurring? Can you smell any ammonia gas in the flask?

The combination of these two gases is evidently a problem. We shall try to find out why.

18.3. Starting with ammonia

Let us tackle the problem from the other end. Perhaps too much sparking destroys ammonia in the same way as too much heat destroys sulphur trioxide. Your teacher will fill a special test-tube with mercury (Figure 83) and invert it in a small dish of mercury (Figure 84).

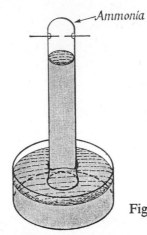

Pass in dry ammonia gas until there is about one inch of it in the top of the test-tube (Figure 85). You can get ammonia gas by warming ammonia solution. The gas is dried by passing it through a tube packed with quicklime (Figure 86).

Figures 85

Now spark this ammonia for one minute. Do you see any change in the appearance of the gas in the test-tube? Do you see any change in its volume?

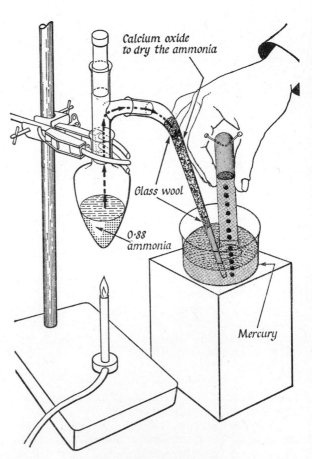

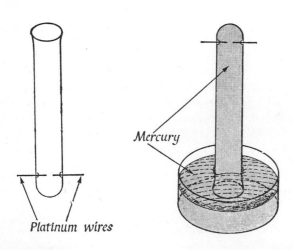

Figure 83   Figure 84   Figure 86

Mark the new level of the mercury and repeat the sparking until there is no further change in volume. Let the apparatus cool. What has happened to the gas volume? How does it compare with the original volume of ammonia?

Put a lighted taper in the gas which is left. What is the result? Can you suggest what has happened to the ammonia to cause the change in volume?

Since we have found that decomposing ammonia causes an increase in volume, perhaps an increase in pressure will favour the formation of ammonia by reducing the volume. Let us follow up this idea.

18.4. Making ammonia

In 17.1, p. 70 when we faced the problem of having to combine sulphur dioxide and oxygen, we discussed the idea of chemical equilibrium. In our experiments with ammonia we might have a similar situation.

Sparking ammonia gives the reaction—

$$2NH_3 \rightarrow N_2 + 3H_2$$

while combining nitrogen with hydrogen by increasing the pressure might give the reaction—

$$N_2 + 3H_2 \rightarrow 2NH_3$$

The chemical equilibrium in this case would be—

$$N_2 + 3H_2 \rightleftharpoons 2NH_3$$

One set of conditions drives the reaction from left to right and different conditions drive it from right to left.

To form ammonia it is likely that a nitrogen-hydrogen mixture has to be compressed. This crowds the molecules together thus increasing the chance of collision, in the same way as crowding people together increases the chance of one bumping into another.

Since very high temperatures destroy ammonia (18.3) the temperature will have to be kept down during combination. In practice the pressure reached can be over 1000 atmospheres while the temperature is in the region of 500°C. The higher the pressure the more ammonia is formed.

You have met the idea of a catalyst—something which speeds up a reaction by providing a large surface area to which the reacting gases are attracted before they combine. In the production of ammonia, an iron catalyst is used.

Once ammonia has been formed it is quickly removed before it has a chance to decompose. This can be done by condensing the gas using a freezing mixture of solid carbon dioxide and alcohol. This mixture is a convenient way of producing temperatures as low as −78°C. The liquid ammonia is then drawn off. You can see how this works if you set up the apparatus shown in Figure 87.

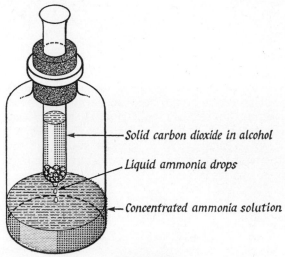

Solid carbon dioxide in alcohol

Liquid ammonia drops

Concentrated ammonia solution

Figure 87

The ammonia gas condenses on the outside of the test-tube and you can see drops of liquid ammonia collecting.

This important industrial manufacture of ammonia is called **the Haber process**—after the German chemist who first successfully carried out the combination. Nowadays the nitrogen required is obtained from producer gas, while the hydrogen is obtained from water gas or from a reaction between petroleum and steam about which we shall have more to say next year.

18.5. Ammonia and water

Ammonia is very soluble in water. Has the solution any effect on litmus?

This indicates that ammonia does not simply dissolve in water but reacts with it to produce hydroxyl ions. Let us try to find additiona evidence for this theory.

Test a solution of distilled water with the conductivity apparatus. Dissolve two test-tubes of ammonia gas in the water and test the conductivity again. Have ions been formed? If so, where can they have come from? To answer this question we must look again at the structures of molecules of ammonia and water (Figures 88 and 89).

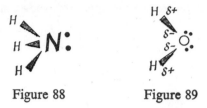

Figure 88   Figure 89

The pair of electrons on the nitrogen atom, which are not employed in forming a bond, occupy an electron pair cloud. The hydrogen atoms in the water molecule have a slightly positive charge. One of them is induced to join this cloud and form a new ion—the ammonium ion (Figures 90 and 91).

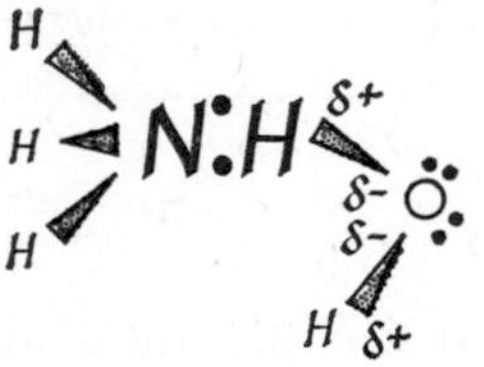

Figure 90

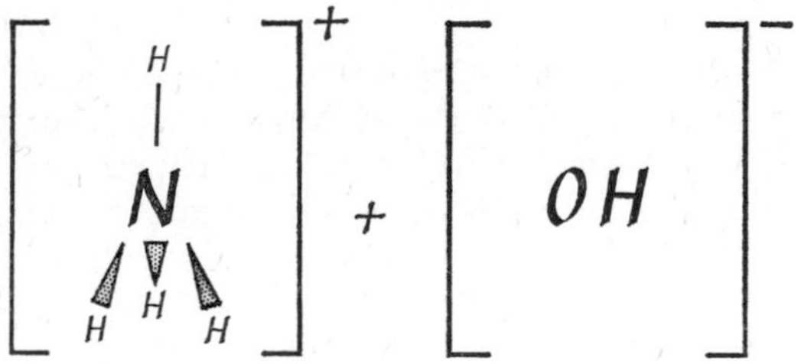

Figure 91

It is the build-up of hydroxyl ions which gives the alkaline properties to a solution of ammonia in water. The solution is called ammonium hydroxide.

You should notice that the covalent bond between the nitrogen atom and the hydrogen ion removed from the water molecule, is formed from two electrons *both* of which come from the nitrogen atom in ammonia (Figure 88). This bond is called a **co-ordinate bond** to distinguish it from

a normal covalent bond formed by two electrons' one of which comes from each of the atoms which it joins. It behaves in exactly the same way as the other three covalent bonds in the ammonium ion. This ion has a tetrahedral shape.

There is no practical difference between the four covalent bonds in the ion.

18.6. How many ions?

Your teacher will give you molar solutions of sodium hydroxide and ammonium hydroxide. Test the conductivity of equal volumes of each using the conductivity apparatus. Which is the better conductor? The apparatus you used is not sensitive enough to show the difference in mobility between the sodium ions and the ammonium ions. Can you suggest why the two solutions have different conducting powers?

When solid sodium hydroxide, Na^+OH^-, dissolves in water, free sodium ions and hydroxyl ions pass into solution. None of these ions remains locked together. A base which behaves like this is called a **strong base**.

On the other hand, a solution of ammonium hydroxide of the same concentration contains fewer ions. It is a **weak base**. At any one time many of the ammonium ions and hydroxyl ions are combined to give ammonia and water.

$$NH_3 + H_2O \rightleftharpoons NH_4^+ + OH^-$$

most of the solution   very few ions are
is probably in this form   free at any one time

LOOKING BACK AT CHAPTER 18

Before you leave this chapter, you should *know* and *understand* the meaning of the following:
  1. Haber Process.
  2. Ammonium Ion.
  3. Co-ordinate Bond.
  4. Strong and Weak Bases.

19 FROM A USEFUL BASE TO A USEFUL ACID

In Chapter 18 we learned about the major break-through that was achieved when nitrogen and hydrogen were directly combined to give ammonia. The combination of nitrogen and oxygen to give nitric oxide (NO) and nitrogen dioxide (NO_2) consumed much electrical energy and so the process was not very efficient.

Chemists decided to try to make the oxides of nitrogen by reacting ammonia with oxygen.

19.1. Burning ammonia

Very early in our study of chemistry we found that burning substances in air caused oxides to form. Burning magnesium gave magnesium oxide and burning sulphur gave sulphur dioxide. Would burning ammonia give nitrogen dioxide?

Prepare some dry ammonia on a small scale as shown in the sketch (Figure 92).

Try to set the ammonia alight by bringing a bunsen up to the jet. Does it burn? Remove the bunsen. Does it continue to burn? Is there any sign of the brown fumes of nitrogen dioxide?

Perhaps it will burn better if the oxygen supply is improved. Surround the jet with a slow stream of oxygen (Figure 93). Does it burn better? Are there any brown fumes? Test the air above the flame with moist blue litmus.

Burning ammonia

Oxygen

Figure 93

19.2. Supplying oxygen from another compound

A readily reduced oxide, such as copper (II) oxide, is sometimes used as a source of oxygen in chemical reactions.

Try passing a stream of dry ammonia over a bed of hot copper (II) oxide (Figure 94). What happens to the oxide? Do you see any brown fumes? Has the water in the beaker become acid because NO_2 has dissolved in it? Is any gas collecting in the test-tube? Look closely at the outlet end of the combustion tube. Has any product gathered there?

From your own observations complete this equation in your notebook.

$$NH_3 + Cu^{2+} + O^{2-} \rightarrow$$

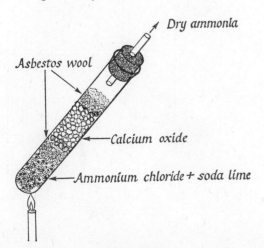

Dry ammonia

Asbestos wool

Calcium oxide

Ammonium chloride + soda lime

Figure 92

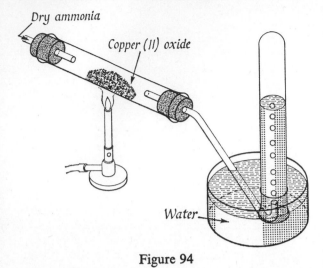

Figure 94

19.3. Does a catalyst help?

So far, our attempts to obtain nitrogen dioxide by the oxidation of ammonia have not been very successful. The hydrogen of the ammonia has readily combined with the oxygen, but the inactive nitrogen has reverted to nitrogen gas.

With the aid of a catalyst it may be possible to make the nitrogen of the ammonia combine with oxygen.

An apparatus like this (Figure 95) or one modified to suit the apparatus you have, should be of some use. A gentle stream of air from a foot or hand bellows is passed over the ammonia solution picking up ammonia gas. The air-ammonia mixture, to get out of the side-arm tube, must pass through the warm platinised asbestos. When the asbestos begins to glow take away the bunsen. What do you notice about the catalyst? The gases coming from the reaction tube are likely to contain some unchanged ammonia and so the mixture is passed up a tower of calcium chloride which is an ammonia absorber and a drying agent. Do any brown fumes arrive in the large collecting jar?

This process is again an important one and is called after its inventor **Ostwald**.

Industrially, the air-ammonia mixture is passed up through a series of large platinum gauzes—each about 6 ft in diameter and costing about £10,000. The reaction is sufficiently exothermic to maintain the platinum catalyst at a temperature high enough (800°C) for it to operate efficiently.

Once more a catalyst has been found which makes a desirable chemical reaction a practical reality.

19.4. A monobasic (monoprotic) acid

In your earlier work (3.5, p. 12) you found that dilute nitric acid had a high electrical conductivity showing that it was highly ionised in water.

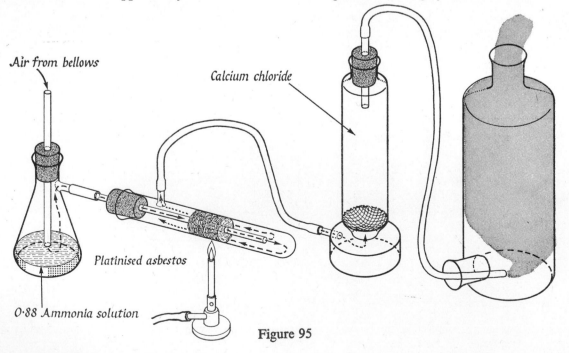

Figure 95

The nitric acid prepared by the action of concentrated sulphuric acid on a nitrate (17.4, p. 72) is extremely concentrated and seems to be composed largely of un-ionised hydrogen nitrate. We shall see some evidence for this later in this chapter.

The acid which is commercially sold as concentrated nitric acid is about 70% concentrated (about 17 M). This acid is extremely corrosive to most common materials such as wood, skin, clothing and paper and therefore you must handle it very carefully.

Again your teacher may demonstrate these reactions in the interests of your safety.

You should take this opportunity of preparing one of the salts of nitric acid and later we shall use the product for another experiment. The salt is *ammonium nitrate*. You will have to decide upon an indicator. When you have titrated the ammonium hydroxide with the nitric acid, note the volume of acid used for the 25 ml of ammonium hydroxide. Reject the solution and repeat the titration without an indicator using the known volume of nitric acid. The salt obtained will then not be coloured by the indicator. Evaporate the solution, but not to dryness. Cover and allow it to crystallise. If your teacher gives you the molarity of the acid, calculate the molarity of the ammonium hydroxide. The ammonium nitrate will be required in 19.8, p. 82.

19.5. Nitric acid, the electron acceptor

Like sulphuric acid, nitric acid accepts electrons in more than one way.

Place an nch of water in a test-tube and drop in a piece of magnesium ribbon. Describe any reaction you see. With a dropper add *one* drop of concentrated nitric acid. Is there any change now? If necessary, add another drop or two of the concentrated acid until bubbles of gas are streaming from the magnesium. Identify the gas.

Add a little more of the concentrated acid until another change occurs in the reaction. Is the same gas being given off? What is happening near the mouth of the test-tube?

Pour away the solution and rinse it carefully down the drain with plenty of cold water.

Put a fresh piece of magnesium into the test-tube and add a few drops of concentrated nitric acid directly to it. What is the result this time?

What evidence is there for the formation of magnesium ions?

There have been at least three different gases given off, depending upon the concentration of the acid.

Repeat the experiment with a small piece of copper foil. What are the results this time? Why do they differ from the magnesium results? Now let us sum up.

(i) *Very dilute nitric acid*

$$Mg \rightarrow Mg^{2+} + 2e$$
$$2e + 2H^+ \rightarrow H_2$$
from the
dilute acid

This is the reaction one would expect with a **mazit** metal and an acid. With copper there can be no hydrogen because it is below hydrogen in the reactivity series.

(ii) *Dilute nitric acid*

$$Mg \rightarrow Mg^{2+} + 2e$$
$$\text{or } Cu \rightarrow Cu^{2+} + 2e$$

The ion-electron equation showing the acceptance of these electrons is a little more complicated and so we shall build it up step by step. The nitrate ion has given the gas nitric oxide (NO) which is colourless.

$$NO_3^- \rightarrow NO$$

There are *two* oxygen atoms more on the left of the equation than on the right. But nitrate ions are accompanied by hydrogen ions from the dilute nitric acid. By adding *four* hydrogen ions to the left, the extra oxygen is combined as water shown on the right of the equation.

$$\underbrace{NO_3^- + 4H^+}_{\text{total charge}=+3} \rightarrow \underbrace{NO + 2H_2O}_{\text{total charge}=0}$$

You will notice that there is a difference in electrical charge on either side of the equation. But electrons are being supplied by the metal. When three electrons join the left of the equation, the charge is balanced.

$$\underset{\substack{\text{from the}\\\text{metal}}}{3e} + \underset{\substack{\text{from the acid}}}{NO_3^-} + 4H^+ \rightarrow NO + 2H_2O$$

This is an attempt to express a complicated reaction as an equation but it does not follow that this is the actual route that the reaction takes.

(iii) *Fairly concentrated nitric acid*

$$Mg \rightarrow Mg^{2+} + 2e$$
and $Cu \rightarrow Cu^{2+} + 2e$

But this time the product is the brown gas nitrogen dioxide (NO_2) instead of nitric oxide (NO). We shall try to express this as follows.

$$NO_3^- \rightarrow NO_2$$

There is extra oxygen on the left and so we shall use two hydrogen ions from the acid to remove it as water.

$$\underbrace{NO_3^- + 2H^+}_{\text{total charge} = +1} \rightarrow \underbrace{NO_2 + H_2O}_{\text{total charge} = 0}$$

By supplying an electron from the metal to the left-hand side, we shall make the equation balance electrically.

$$\underset{\substack{\text{from the} \\ \text{metal}}}{e} + \underset{\text{from the acid}}{NO_3^-} + 2H^+ \rightarrow NO_2 + H_2O$$

These three products, hydrogen, nitric oxide and nitrogen dioxide are not the only ones possible nor do they always appear alone. There is often a mixture of them depending upon the concentration of the acid.

Summary diagram

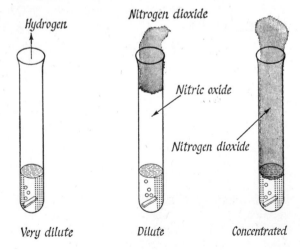

Hydrogen

Nitrogen dioxide

Nitric oxide

Nitrogen dioxide

Very dilute   *Dilute*   *Concentrated*

Figure 96

19.6. An unexpected result

Your teacher may show you a rather unexpected reaction of a metal with concentrated nitric acid.

A piece of stainless steel (an alloy of iron and chromium) is placed in a beaker of dilute hydrochloric acid and warmed until bubbles of hydrogen are escaping freely. The bunsen is removed and a little concentrated nitric acid is added. As expected, the nitric acid attacks the metal vigorously, but what happens after a minute or so?

When the metal is examined after the reaction, its surface is dull because a layer of chromium oxide has been formed by the action of the nitric acid. This layer protects the steel from further attack and the steel is said to have been made **passive**. The layer can be dissolved off with hydrochloric acid.

19.7. A pattern in nitrates

Before we return to the industrial importance of nitric acid and nitrates, there is one investigation which you could make to see if the reactivity series has any bearing on the behaviour of nitrates when they are heated. In the case of carbonates, we noticed that the compounds of the most active metals are stable to heat, but as we descend the series, the compounds become less and less stable until eventually heating decomposes the compound down to the metal itself.

Heat a selection of nitrates and try to fit them into some sort of pattern. The solids left after heating potassium and sodium nitrates will require some thought if you are going to identify them. When you think of the formulae of the nitrates, you will have some idea of the gases which are likely to be released and you should be ready to test for them. It is possible that more than one gas will be given off at any one time. Record your results carefully, sift the evidence and try to find a pattern.

19.8. Ammonium nitrate

In 19.4 you prepared some crystals of ammonium nitrate. Filter them off and dry them between sheets of filter paper.

Place a few crystals in a dry test-tube and heat them. Describe what you see. After a while you may get a slight explosion which is quite harmless on this scale. (Ammonium nitrate is sometimes mixed with other high explosives in shells to give a violent explosion.)

What is left in the test-tube?

Repeat the experiment with a few more crystals

to try to identify the gases coming off. Since nothing is left at the end of the reaction, what possible gases could be coming off? Test for them.

When this reaction is done on a large scale with special precautions, the gas can be collected over water. It has a sweet smell showing that it is not oxygen and yet it shares one of the properties of oxygen. Which? This is another oxide of nitrogen called nitrous oxide (N_2O) or 'laughing gas'. It is the gas used by dentists as an anaesthetic. It seldom causes laughter!

LOOKING BACK AT CHAPTER 19

Before you leave this chapter, you should *know* and *understand* the meaning of the following:
1. Oxidation of Ammonia.
2. Very dilute nitric acid as an electron acceptor.
3. Dilute nitric acid as an electron acceptor.
4. Concentrated nitric acid as an electron acceptor.
5. Balancing ion-electron equations.

Something to think about

1. When fresh and very concentrated nitric acid is poured on a piece of copper, little or no reaction seems to take place. The addition of a little water causes a vigorous reaction to start. Try to explain this.
2. If you can find a copy of *Young Chemists and Great Discoveries* by J. P. Kendall you will find how laughing gas got its name.

THE IMPORTANCE OF NITROGEN 20

20.1. The nitrogen cycle

Plants and animals (including ourselves) require a supply of combined nitrogen for the growth and repair of their bodies. They are unable to use the nitrogen of the air to form protein which is the main tissue building substance. Animals get this combined nitrogen by eating other animals, or by eating plants which have been grown in ground containing compounds like ammonium nitrate or ammonium sulphate.

Figure 97

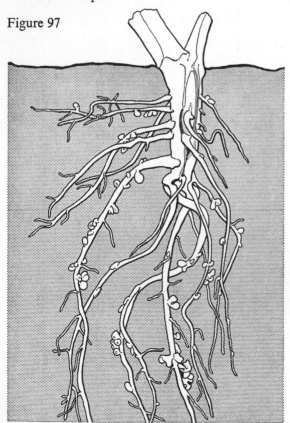

There are a few plants, including clover and bean (members of the leguminosae family), which *can* use atmospheric nitrogen to build protein. Have you ever dug up a bean plant and observed little swellings on the roots (Figure 97)?

These contain bacteria which have a very special role. They convert the free or uncombined nitrogen of the air into a form which can be used by the plant to which they are attached. They are referred to as **nitrifying** bacteria. Exactly how they do this is not known but they evidently manage it more readily than the chemist does!

One of the rules of chemistry is that something cannot be made from nothing. In growing our crops we cannot continue to draw nitrogen compounds from the soil without putting some back.

We must establish a nitrogen cycle—something like the carbon dioxide cycle which we encountered last year. How do we return nitrogen compounds to the soil?

In a very small farm or croft it is possible to do this if the nitrogen compounds are put back on the soil in the form of animal manure and compost. Another idea would be to sow the fields with clover every few years.

All this information can be neatly summed up in a diagram (Figure 98). Try to follow it step by step.

However, this return of nitrogen compounds to the soil is not easy in our modern industrial civilisation. The farms producing our food are often a thousand miles or more away from where the food is being consumed. There is no chance of the refuse being put back into the soil of the original food producing area.

There is, therefore, one very important difference between the carbon dioxide cycle and any nitrogen cycle. The former carries on unhindered by man because the gas, carbon dioxide, is circulated round the world by winds and oceans. A

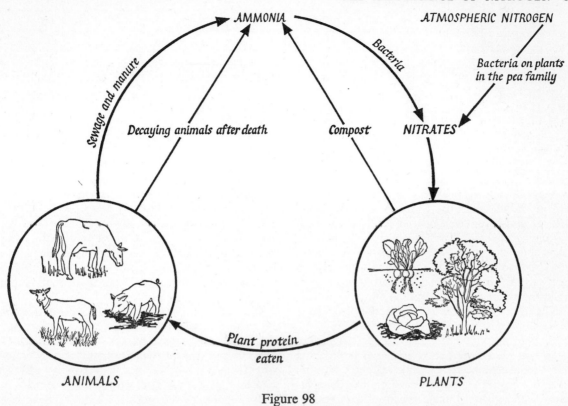

Figure 98

nitrogen cycle, however, involves solid materials such as manures and compost, and if man does not go to the trouble of ploughing them back into the soil, this cycle *can be broken*. The consequences of this are extremely serious and in many parts of the world the state of permanent famine is due, in part, to the ignorance of farmers about the facts of the nitrogen cycle.

As far back as 1898, Sir William Crookes saw that the food producing areas of North America would become steadily poorer if they continued to export food without returning manure to the soil. He forecast a famine in Europe and North America by 1930. Here are some extracts from his lecture.

'My chief subject is of interest to the whole world—to every race—to every human being. It is of urgent importance to-day, and it is a life and death question for generations to come. I mean the question of food supply. Many of my statements you may think are of the alarmist order; certainly they are depressing, but they are founded on stubborn facts. They show that England and all civilised nations stand in deadly peril of not having enough to eat. As mouths multiply, food resources dwindle.'

'I have said that starvation may be averted through the laboratory.'

'Much has been said of late years, and many hopes raised by the discovery of Hellriegel and Wilfarth, that leguminous plants bear on their roots nodosities abounding in bacteria endowed with the property of fixing atmospheric nitrogen; and it is proposed that the necessary amount of nitrogen demanded by grain crops should be supplied to the soil by cropping it with clover and ploughing in the plant when its nitrogen assimilation is complete. But it is questionable whether such a mode of procedure will lead to the lucrative stimulation of crops. It must be admitted that practice has long been ahead of science, and for ages farmers have valued and cultivated leguminous crops. The four-course rotation is turnips, barley, clover, wheat—a sequence popular more than two thousand years ago.'

'There is still another and invaluable source of fixed nitrogen. I mean the treasure locked up in the sewage and drainage of our towns. Individually the amount so lost is trifling, but multiply the loss by the number of inhabitants, and we have the startling fact that, in the United Kingdom, we are content to hurry down our drains and water courses, into the sea, fixed nitrogen to the value of no less than £16,000,000 per annum. This unspeakable waste continues, and no effective and universal method is yet contrived of converting sewage into corn.'

'The more widely this wasteful system is extended, recklessly returning to the sea what we have taken from the land, the more surely and quickly will the finite stocks of nitrogen locked up in the soils of the world become exhausted.

'The fixation of atmospheric nitrogen therefore, is one of the great discoveries awaiting the ingenuity of chemists. It is certainly deeply important in its practical bearings on the future welfare and happiness of the civilised races of mankind. This unfulfilled problem, which so far has eluded the strenuous attempts of those who have tried to wrest the secret from nature, differs materially from other chemical discoveries which are in the air, so to speak, but are not yet matured. The fixation of nitrogen is vital to the progress of civilised humanity.'

His warning was heeded and steps were taken to put nitrogen compounds back into the soil. At first, the large deposits of Chile saltpetre (sodium nitrate) were imported as fertiliser, but chemists were challenged to make nitrogen compounds from the abundant nitrogen of the air. How tantalising it was to see soil becoming impoverished for lack of nitrogen compounds while above each square yard there were seven tons of atmospheric nitrogen waiting to be used!

How the problem was overcome is one of the major scientific achievements of all time.

At first chemists tried to copy nature and create lightning in the laboratory. This formed oxides of nitrogen, some of which dissolved in water to form a solution of nitric acid which could be used to make nitrates. Although this was an answer to the problem, when it was carried out on the industrial scale to produce large tonnages of calcium nitrate, it proved an inefficient and expensive process.

But a better answer was forthcoming—hastened by a world war! In 1914 Germany was blockaded and instead of importing nitrates, which also found a use as explosives, she had to make her own. Here was another reason for wanting to convert atmospheric nitrogen into nitrates—a spur to Fritz Haber!

When Haber succeeded in converting atmospheric nitrogen to ammonia, the way was clear to make vast quantities of both ammonium compounds and nitric acid from readily available elements. A tremendous problem was solved!

It is interesting to note that, at the present time, about 85% of the ammonia produced in the world ends up as fertilisers and that about one million tons of ammonium sulphate is produced annually in Great Britain alone.

However, having said all this, two notes of caution must be sounded.

(a) We must not misunderstand the word 'food'. Most of what has been said applies to the production of grain crops, which are our main sources of carbohydrate (starchy) foods. But 'food' in the nutritional sense must contain proteins. The fixation of nitrogen has improved the production of carbohydrate foods without necessarily improving our sources of protein because mature grain contains less protein than we need to maintain good health. In some parts of the world starvation is not so much caused by lack of carbohydrate as by an inadequate supply of protein.

(b) The process of nitrogen fixation requires large amounts of fuel. To fix "the seven tons of nitrogen above every acre of land" requires at least twenty tons of fuel. Our fuel reserves cannot last for ever and so the problem of nitrogen fixation has not been solved once and for all.

In Figure 99 the points which we have been discussing have been added to Figure 98. This is the important nitrogen cycle.

The farmer has also to prevent the soil from becoming too acid. If this happens the nitrifying bacteria refuse to do their job and instead *denitrifying* bacteria convert the valuable nitrates back into free nitrogen! If you shake a sample of soil from your garden with a little water and filter the mixture, your teacher may give you a piece of indicator paper with which you can find the pH of the soil. You can tell if the nitrifying bacteria are at work! Can you suggest how the farmer could reduce the acidity of his soil?

20.2. Making a fertiliser

Once you have decided on an indicator, you can make some ammonium sulphate using ammonium hydroxide and dilute sulphuric acid. The technique is exactly the same as that employed for making ammonium nitrate in 19.4, p. 81.

Dry the crystals of ammonium sulphate on a piece of filter paper. Perhaps you will be allowed to take them home for your garden.

We saw last year that ammonia is obtained from the dry distillation of coal. Although this ammonia is impure, much of it is mixed with an

Figure 99

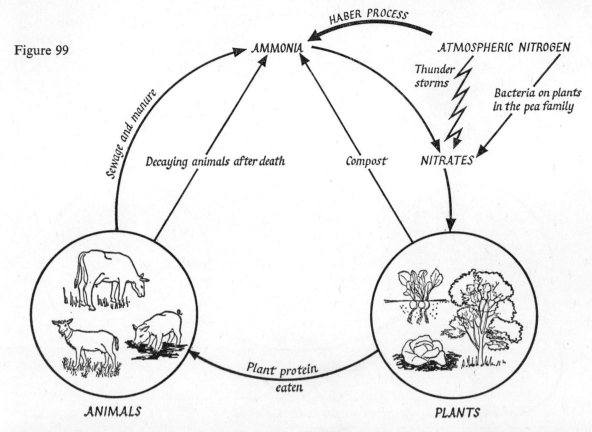

aqueous solution of sulphuric acid to produce ammonium sulphate. The impurities are not harmful.

Although ammonium nitrate contains more nitrogen per formula weight than ammonium sulphate, the latter is produced industrially in greater quantities. This is because ammonium nitrate tends to absorb moisture from the air and stick together in lumps, thus making it difficult for farmers to spread it on the ground. It is known that if ammonium nitrate is coated with oil it does not absorb moisture so readily, but this treatment increases the risk of explosion. It has been known for ships loaded with thousands of tons of ammonium nitrate to explode!

20.3. Another nitrogen containing fertiliser

If the ammonia is dissolved in a solution of phosphoric acid $(2H^+ + HPO_4^{2-})$ ammonium hydrogen phosphate is formed.

$$2NH_3 + 2H^+ + HPO_4^{2-} \rightarrow 2NH_4^+ + HPO_4^{2-}$$

This compound is a fertiliser which, in addition to nitrogen, contains phosphorus, another essential element for the growth of plants and animals.

You will notice from the Periodic Table that it is in the same group or family as nitrogen. We shall say something about phosphatic fertilisers in the next section.

20.4. A phosphorus cycle?

Although phosphorus is an essential element for plant and animal growth, in the free state it can be extremely poisonous.

The bones of animals are composed of the very insoluble compound, calcium phosphate, $(Ca^{2+})_3(PO_4^{3-})_2$. Powdered bone (bone meal) is a very slow acting fertiliser because of its extreme insolubility.

Searching for more soluble phosphorus containing salts, chemists found two ways of converting calcium phosphate into a quicker acting fertiliser.

(a) Superphosphate

This is a mixture of calcium sulphate and the acid salt, calcium dihydrogen phosphate, $Ca^{2+}(H_2PO_4^-)_2$. It is obtained when finely powdered calcium phosphate is thoroughly mixed with fairly concentrated sulphuric acid.

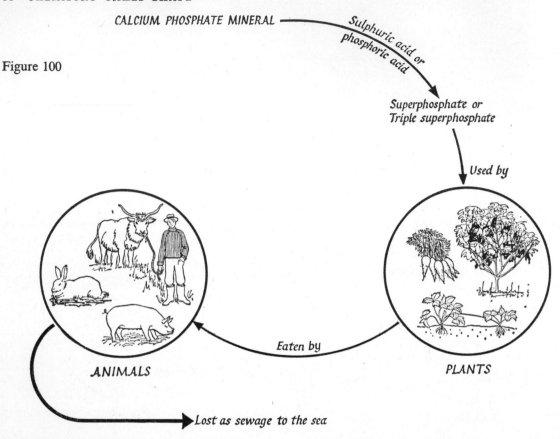

Figure 100

CALCIUM PHOSPHATE MINERAL

Sulphuric acid or phosphoric acid

Superphosphate or
Triple superphosphate

Used by

Eaten by

ANIMALS

PLANTS

Lost as sewage to the sea

(b)   *Triple superphosphate*

The calcium sulphate in superphosphate is an impurity which is of little value and in many countries a more concentrated phosphatic fertiliser with a higher phosphorus content is used. This is called triple superphosphate. It is the acid salt, calcium dihydrogen phosphate, and is produced when calcium phosphate is treated with phosphoric acid instead of with sulphuric acid.

The picture so far

In this country quite large tonnages of super-phosphate are being made, but there is a tendency to make more use of ammonium hydrogen phosphate. It seems likely that within a few years greater tonnages of this compound will be produced as chemists attempt to increase the concentration of fertilisers. You might like to know how it is made on a large scale.

When calcium phosphate mineral is treated with an *excess* of sulphuric acid, superphosphate is not obtained. Instead the insoluble salt,

calcium sulphate, is precipitated and phosphoric acid is formed.

After filtration the phosphoric acid solution is concentrated by evaporation. Ammonium hydrogen phosphate is produced when ammonia gas is absorbed by this acid (20.3).

Adding this to Figure 100 we get a more complete picture.

You will notice that, despite the ingenuity of the chemist, there is no complete phosphorus cycle.

Almost all our phosphorus compounds are flushed into the sea as sewage and lost. Only a very little of it gets back on to the land as fish meal.

There is a limit to our reserves of phosphate rock and in some countries there is a frantic search going on to find new deposits of it because the present rock is running out.

How are we to complete the phosphorus cycle?

From every point of view, the sensible solution to the problem is to use our sewage instead of poisoning rivers with it. There are hygenic

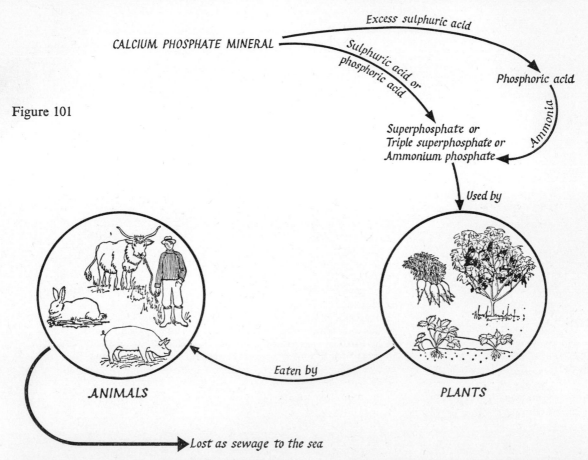

Figure 101

methods of treating sewage to form an excellent fertiliser which is rich in nitrogen compounds and in phosphates. It costs money to build a plant for sewage treatment, but the outlay can be recovered by the sale of fertilisers and fuel gases which are produced during the purification. Some authorities have done this job very efficiently, but many continue to ignore the facts. The chemist has pointed the way and issued the warning.

20.5.   Three interesting comparisons

Your teacher may be able to show you plants which have been grown in sand and watered with solutions deficient in nitrogen and in phosphorus compounds. It is interesting to compare their growth with plants which have been given all the required minerals.

The importance of the fertiliser industry cannot be over emphasised. Millions throughout the world still have not enough to eat. What can be done to improve matters? Chemistry is helping to provide an answer.

One of the latest ideas is to inject anhydrous liquid ammonia, the most concentrated form of nitrogen fertiliser available, directly into the soil.

The research teams in the fertiliser industry are constantly looking for new methods of increasing the world's food supply. Perhaps some day you may share in the search for methods and materials which will benefit mankind.

LOOKING BACK AT CHAPTER 20

Before you leave this chapter, you should *know* and *understand* the meaning of the following:
1. Nitrifying Bacteria.
2. Nitrogen Cycle.
3. Phosphorus Cycle?
4. The importance of sewage.

Something to do

Prepare a chart of newspaper and magazine cuttings which deal with the problem of increasing the world's food supplies.

INDEX

LIST OF COMMON IONS WITH THEIR VALENCY NUMBERS
SHOWN AS A NUMBER OF CHARGES

Fluoride	F^-	Sulphate	SO_4^{2-}	Phosphate	PO_4^{3-}
Chloride	Cl^-	Sulphite	SO_3^{2-}		
Bromide	Br^-	Carbonate	CO_3^{2-}		
Iodide	I^-				
Nitrate	NO_3^-				
Nitrite	NO_2^-				
Hydroxide	OH^-				
Ammonium	NH_4^+				